THE RIGHT HUSBAND

All her life, while Kerry had attracted trouble, Declan was always around to rescue her — an unofficial guardian. She'd almost ended up marrying him. Almost, but not quite. At the eleventh hour her childhood sweetheart turned up to stake his claim to her. After all, Declan's marriage proposal had only been a favour to rescue her from a difficult situation. They weren't really in love . . . Yet jilting Declan at the altar was the hardest thing Kerry had ever done . . .

KAY GREGORY

THE RIGHT HUSBAND

Complete and Unabridged

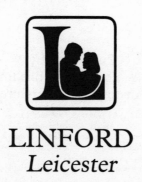

LINFORD
Leicester

First published in Great Britain in 1996

First Linford Edition
published 2012

British Library CIP Data

Gregory, Kay.
  The right husband. - -
  (Linford romance library)
  1. Love stories.
  2. Large type books.
  I. Title II. Series
  813.5′4–dc23

  ISBN 978–1–4448–1180–3

Published by
F. A. Thorpe (Publishing)
Anstey, Leicestershire

Set by Words & Graphics Ltd.
Anstey, Leicestershire
Printed and bound in Great Britain by
T. J. International Ltd., Padstow, Cornwall

This book is printed on acid-free paper

With thanks to Marilyn Gregory
& Bev Prynallt who always read
my books, and to Korri, Kaper
& Sparky for appearing in them.

1

The church was packed. Everyone who was anyone in Carmody Falls had gathered beneath the dim mauve light streaming through the stained-glass windows. Hymn-books rustled and voices whispered in anticipation as the town waited to witness the wedding of Kerry Fleming to Declan King.

When the organ's soothing prologue faded into meaningful silence, and the rustling and the whispering died away, all eyes turned expectantly toward the high stone arch of the entrance.

Declan, standing tall and stiff before the altar, dominated the small church as if he were Gulliver among a congregation of Lilliputians. It wasn't just his height and massive shoulders, or the strongly sculpted contours of his profile. It was something else, some indefinable air of power, of being in control of people and events.

When he turned to his best man and murmured, 'Here comes the bride. Late, as usual,' the best man blinked and looked vaguely uncomfortable.

'She's very — um — pretty though, Declan?'

'Yes. Very,' Declan agreed grimly, as if he saw his pretty bride, not as the woman of his dreams, but as a cross he had made up his mind to shoulder with stern stoicism.

The organ began to play again, the familiar melody announcing the approach of the bride, and the single bridesmaid adjusted her pale yellow headdress, smiled at Kerry, and took the first step of the long walk down the aisle.

After a moment's hesitation, Kerry turned to the white-haired man who stood beaming proudly beside her. 'Here we go, Grandfather,' she whispered.

He nodded, giving her hand a quick pat as he tucked it under his elbow. Then they, too, began to move down the aisle toward the man waiting impassively at the altar.

No eager bridegroom here, thought Kerry with a kind of desperation. Yet it's with him that my destiny lies. With Declan, who is marrying me out of affection, habit, family pride and an unconquerable conviction that he was put on this earth to keep me out of trouble.

The music soared, crashed to a stop. Kerry stepped up beside Declan, who allowed his gaze to roam over her briefly and critically as if neither her deportment nor her bright turquoise wedding gown met with his unqualified approval. Fleetingly, she wondered if she should have chosen more conventional attire. Then decided it didn't matter. Nothing mattered at the moment, except getting through the unreality of this ceremony which would bind her forever to Declan King, the idol of her childhood, despot of her teen years, and now her only refuge in time of trouble.

It was hard, though, to look on Declan, of whom she had always been a little in awe, as a refuge. He was too domineering, had practically ordered her to marry him when he saw there was nowhere else for her to turn. And she was grateful. Of course she was. She was also a little afraid.

And now — she took a deep breath — now there was nothing to do but get on with it.

Kerry swallowed and produced a brave smile. Declan smiled back. It wasn't a comforting smile, yet she had a feeling that for her sake he had decided to put as good a face as possible on the unpalatable business that lay ahead.

Several members of the congregation raised their eyebrows and turned to make whispered comments to puzzled friends.

'Dearly beloved, we are gathered together here in the sight of God . . . ' mumbled the Reverend Jonathan MacNaughton-Bones.

Kerry's grandfather cleared his throat

4

lustily, and for a moment she wondered if he was about to give her away prematurely.

The Reverend Jonathan shook his head and frowned. ' . . . to join together this Man and this Woman, in holy Matrimony . . . Into which holy estate . . . if either of you know any impediment, why ye may not lawfully be joined together . . . ' The words of the marriage ceremony droned relentlessly from the Reverend Jonathan's practiced lips. The bride and groom stared straight ahead, as if the other one didn't exist.

But Kerry was all too aware of Declan's presence. How could she not be? Every slight movement of his body served to remind her of where she would be spending this night. And her own body responded with an instinct that was part excitement and part sheer terror — because in all the years of their growing up together, she had never dared to dream of Declan as a lover. He was too overpowering, too much in command of his world. And sometimes, when she broke the rules he believed in, too much in command of her.

'Wilt thou, Declan John, have this Woman to thy wedded wife . . . and, forsaking all others, keep thee only unto her, so long as ye both shall live?'

'I will.' Declan's voice rang out deep and strong in the sudden stillness, and from behind them came a low murmur of relief.

'Wilt thou, Kerry Ellen, have this Man to thy wedded husband, to live together after God's ordinance in the holy estate of Matrimony — ?'

'No!' shouted a voice from the back of the church. 'She damn well won't. Kerry, wait. Don't do it.'

The assembled congregation let out a united gasp, then relapsed into mesmerized silence as a young man carrying a motorcycle helmet and wearing a black leather jacket, hurled himself down the aisle, grabbed the bride by the arm and said, 'Kerry, you

6

can't marry him. You've got to marry me.'

'Thank God he's not riding a white charger. Or waving his broadsword,' drawled Declan, whose jaw had turned exceptionally rocklike, but who otherwise seemed astonishingly unmoved.

Kerry said nothing. She couldn't. Her mouth had gone dry, her heart was jumping like an intoxicated cricket, and she wasn't sure her legs would hold her up.

'Kerry?' said the newcomer. 'Kerry, answer me.'

'She can't,' said Declan coldly. 'Your timing has rendered her speechless.'

'No.' Kerry found her voice, although it came out sounding strained and unnatural. 'No, it hasn't. I — I can talk.'

'Good,' said Declan. 'In that case, my dearest not-quite-wife, I'm afraid you are now faced with a decision. Our guests may, or may not, be particular about whom you marry, but they are expecting you to marry someone. And it would be a shame to waste a perfectly good reception.'

'But . . . ' Kerry bit her lip, dug her nails hard into her palms. She had said she could talk. And she could. But she no longer knew what to say. If Larry had come only a few seconds later she would have been married to Declan. For better, or maybe for worse. But now she had been given a way out. Declan had told her *she* must make the decision. And although it wasn't likely he would relish being jilted in front of the whole town, it was also painfully obvious that he was only marrying her because he felt it to be his duty. He had always had a rigid sense of duty . . .

'Declan,' she finally managed to blurt, 'you don't *care* whether I marry you or not? Do you?' She gazed into the midnight-blue eyes that had always seen right through her and looked for some sign of tenderness, for some indication that he *did* care. But instead he smiled, that crooked, wickedly self-mocking smile that when she was very young had

8

always made her want to hug him. She wouldn't have dared to hug him now.

'Certainly I care,' he replied. 'Marriage, especially to you, isn't the sort of thing I'd be inclined to drift into by mistake. But young Lochinvar here is, after all, the father of the child I was planning to give my name to.' He ran a dauntingly hard eye over the stocky figure of the other man and demanded, 'Why the sudden change of heart?'

'I love her, Sir.' Larry, looking scared but desperately sincere, placed a melodramatic hand on his chest.

'I see.' Declan continued his scrutiny. Then, after a silence so electric Kerry expected lightning to strike the church at any moment, he nodded, as if his doubts had been resolved. 'All right. It seems you've come to your senses.' He turned to Kerry. 'Now that he's put his mind to it, there's no reason he can't manage to take care of you. It's his right and most certainly his responsibility — even though 'the bride has consented, the gallant come late.'' He raised a hand and touched his knuckles to her chin. 'But I'm damned if I'm making this decision for you, Kerry. This time, sweetheart, you're on your own.'

Kerry stared at this mocking, controlled man who had just affirmed his willingness to hand her over to another. His eyes were hooded now, so she couldn't tell what he was thinking, but she didn't need to see his eyes to know that he had never much wanted to marry her. He was a hard man, and over the years had become harder, if the rumours about his business dealings were true. And yet — he *had* been prepared to take on a woman he obviously still thought of as a thoughtless, exasperating child.

She took in his neatly cut dark brown hair, his classically straight nose, and the blue-black eyes she had never yet been able to deceive. He was handsome, in a carved, angular sort of way, but at this moment his firm, surprisingly sensuous lips looked about as inviting as a flytrap. And he was looking at Larry as if the younger man were little more than a bug the church cleaners had overlooked. A bug, though, that he was prepared to let her marry once he'd satisfied himself she'd be looked after.

He *didn't* care. Not in the way a husband is supposed to care for his wife. He would probably be relieved to be rid of her. Why, he'd talked of her marrying Larry instead of him as if he were discussing a transfer of doubtful stock options — not the woman who was about to become his wife.

Kerry lowered her eyelids. She couldn't bear to look at Declan any longer. He didn't want her. He had offered to marry her out of a sense of obligation, and because he was in the habit of organizing her life. She had almost forgotten that painful reality in the days leading up to the wedding, especially when he had smiled his irresistible smile and exercised the potent, easy charm that had drawn her

11

to him right from the beginning.

Slowly Kerry turned to the other man, her laughing, loving, lighthearted, handsome Larry. Her lover with the streaky blond hair and the engaging, little-boy smile. Larry, who never frowned and looked disapproving, or told her to stop giggling and behave. Larry who had deserted her when she needed him most, but who now, when it was almost too late, had come back to make her his wife.

His eyes had gone all soft and pleading. His little-boy mouth was tender. 'I love you, Kerry,' he murmured. 'Please forgive me. Please — marry me.'

Kerry stole one last look at Declan. There was no softness there, no sign that he would mind if she left him.

She turned back to Larry. 'I forgive you,' she whispered.

She couldn't do anything else.

Declan seemed to know her decision even before she made it. Kerry saw, with a feeling that was part relief, part resentment and part guilty confusion and regret, that he was studying the vaulted ceiling with an expression that indicated exasperation at the sudden change of plan, but nothing remotely resembling hurt or disappointment.

When he turned to look down at her, he said, 'Goodbye, Kerry,' in a voice that was as brisk and unmoved as it might have been if she'd canceled a dinner date. Then, briefly, his features softened, and he flashed his mocking white smile. 'Behave yourself.' To Larry, he added curtly, 'Take care of her. You'll have your hands full.'

Then he gave Kerry a quick peck on the cheek and strode to the back of the church.

Ten minutes later, in front of a stunned congregation, Kerry Fleming became Mrs. Lawrence Simms.

Whether or not Declan stayed to witness his bride marry another man, Kerry never knew. She was too busy gazing in misty-eyed confusion at the smiling youth who had returned, like

13

some fairy-tale prince, to rescue her from a marriage of desperation.

She was not, after all, fated to marry the stern, overbearing man who all her life had treated her as she imagined an affectionate but repressive older brother might treat his mischievous and much younger sister. Yet if anyone had told her, even a week ago, that she would feel the slightest twinge of regret at the thought of not marrying Declan King, she would probably have laughed in their face.

So why did she suddenly feel like crying?

Kerry lifted her chin, gave Larry a tremulous smile. It was better this way. Of course it was. Better for her, better for Larry, who said he loved her — and certainly better for Declan who hadn't wanted to marry her in the first place.

She took Larry's hand in hers and slowly raised her lips for his kiss.

2

Snow followed Kerry into the restaurant. It swirled around her in icy white flakes until she turned and slammed the door behind her.

Inside it was warm. A clean, dry warmth that smelled of soap and cedar. Kerry pushed back the hood of her blue parka and made her way toward the counter. But as she navigated around the tables, she was conscious of curious glances and patrons nudging each other in the ribs.

Carmody Falls had not forgotten her then. Scandal must be in short supply this Easter. She sighed. Surely it had been reasonable to hope that after seven years people might have moved on to other, more up-to-date gossip. But it seemed they hadn't.

'Kerry Fleming!' exclaimed a grizzled patriarch with a face that reminded her of knotted oak. 'You haven't changed a bit.'

She had. She was slimmer now, and her straight blond hair with the unruly flipped-up ends had taken on a darker, more honeyed hue as she grew older. But obviously her appearance hadn't changed sufficiently to deceive the inhabitants of this close-knit, Northern Ontario community.

'Yes,' she said to the patriarch. 'It's me. How are you, Barney?'

'Couldn't be better.' The old man's gaze followed her as she smiled guardedly and passed by him on her way to take a seat at the polished, semicircular counter that took up most of the far wall. She was conscious of a whole set of eyes boring into her back. They weren't friendly eyes. The customers lounging at the tables were the modern equivalent of village elders, and they had never approved of the lighthearted and often troublesome antics of the girl she had been before she married Larry. She supposed she couldn't blame them for looking at her as if she were a deer with designs on their rose bushes, but she still found their scrutiny irksome.

It wasn't until she sat down that she noticed the man nursing a coffee directly across from her on the other side of the U formed by the counter. A lean, well-built man with a lean, angular face that shouldn't have been handsome but was.

Kerry gasped. It couldn't be. Lori had written that he hadn't been seen in Carmody Falls for years. She looked away, then back again, not believing her eyes, hoping he would turn out to be an illusion. Or somebody who wasn't Declan King.

But when she forced herself to study him more closely she had no choice but to accept that the man she was gaping at was no illusion. Illusions didn't wear expensive navy pullovers or emit a kind of personal magnetism by the mere act of raising a cup to chiseled lips.

She remembered those lips. They had

never seriously kissed her, but for a few confused and dreamlike weeks she had thought that very soon they would.

He was more mature now, of course, and his dark brown hair was longer than she remembered. But there was no mistaking that firm, aggressive jaw — or the thick lashes shielding the blue-black eyes that had always seen right through her.

'Well, well. If it isn't the lost bride of Netherby,' drawled Declan. 'Hello, Kerry Ellen. Home for Easter?'

She shook her head, and when she spoke, her voice was uneven, almost husky. 'I was. But now I can't stay.'

He raised his eyebrows in that way that, as a teenager, she had found particularly intimidating. 'Can't you?' he said. 'Not leaving on my account, I hope?'

Kerry blushed. She tried hard not to blush these days, but she had every reason to feel self-conscious about the way she had behaved the last time she and Declan had been this close. It wasn't something either of them was likely to forget.

'No,' she replied, with an irritation born of embarrassment. 'Of course I'm not. Don't flatter yourself, Declan. I came to spend Easter with Lori and her family. But when I got here they were all down with chicken pox.'

'Lori?' Declan strummed his fingers on the counter. 'Ah, yes, the young lady in yellow who was a bridesmaid at our almost-wedding.'

'Yes,' said Kerry shortly.

'And she has chicken pox?'

'She has it, her husband has it, and both the kids have it. So I couldn't stay.'

'Of course not. Florence Nightingale was never one of your roles, as I remember.'

'That's not . . . ' She lowered her voice, as half a dozen heads turned in her direction. 'That's not fair, Declan. Lori didn't want me around. I've never had chicken pox and she said she was very sorry, but that in her case misery hates company and could I possibly

19

find somewhere else to stay?'

When all the necks belonging to the heads craned forward, she realized it was going to be impossible to carry on a private conversation. Not that she wanted a private conversation. At one time Declan had been her friend, confidant and beloved mentor. She would have crawled through broken glass to please him. And he would have rescued her from the glass. But too much had happened since those days. Now, if he left her to bleed, she wouldn't blame him.

'I'd better go,' she said, sliding off her stool.

'Kerry Fleming! Leaving already? You city people sure are impatient.' A large young man with ginger hair wandered out from the kitchen wiping his hands on a striped dish towel. 'What's your hurry, Kerry?'

'I'm sorry, Phil. I have to go.' She looked around, searching for a polite way to escape without causing offence. 'Um — you always said you'd make this place into something special. And I see you have. The food smells great. I just didn't realize it was getting so late.'

'I've scared her away,' said Declan, leaning back in his chair and exchanging a caustic grin with the large man. 'Sorry, Phil.'

'Huh.' Phil snorted. 'Kerry always was a smart one. Some girls don't have the sense to know trouble when they see it on two feet.' He gave Declan a man-to-man wink then added ruefully, 'Maybelle, for instance.'

'Oh, Kerry knows trouble, all right,' Declan said softly. 'Don't you, Kerry?'

Kerry turned quickly and began to stumble for the door. That was really hitting below the belt. It wasn't like Declan to be cruel. But of course he owed her nothing. If anything it was the other way around. And what did she really know about the kind of man her childhood idol had turned into in the years since she had abandoned him at the altar?

Only that his name featured frequently on the financial pages of the daily papers in connection with various enormously successful transfers of large sums of money. And that he lived in Toronto in an architectural show-place that was frequently featured in upscale magazines.

She found the door, staggered briefly as she was pushed back by the driving force of wind and snow, then forced her way out into the night.

For a moment the cold stole her breath. She paused to draw it back into her lungs. Then wished she hadn't. Because almost at once the door behind her slammed, and she felt a hard hand lock onto her shoulder.

'This way,' said Declan, propeling her ahead of him up the street as if he imagined she ran on greased wheels. 'I'm staying at the Cambrian.'

'That's nice. I'm not,' said Kerry, trying to dislodge his hand and not succeeding.

'No? Where *are* you staying?' He

made no attempt to change course, but continued to march her along the slippery sidewalk.

'I'm not sure,' she admitted grudgingly. 'Everyone I used to know has either moved or gone away for Easter. Or else they already have a houseful of guests.'

'The Cambrian it is then,' he said decisively. 'No restaurant there, but it's the best Carmody Falls has to offer.'

'Yes, but . . . ' Kerry bit her lip.

'What's the matter? Afraid I'll come prowling down the hall to exact revenge? If I'd wanted to do that, don't you think I'd have seen to it years ago?'

'No.' Kerry gasped as a gust of wind blew snow into her face. 'No, you wouldn't. If you'd cared, you'd never have let me marry Larry in the first place.'

'You've got that right.' There was a steely note in his voice now. 'I wouldn't.' He turned her in the direction of a lighted doorway. 'Here we are. I'll see if they can give us an extra room.'

'Declan,' she protested, as he opened the heavy glass doors and shoved her unceremoniously into the warmth of a red-carpeted lobby festooned with pink paper cutouts of Easter rabbits, 'Declan, wait.'

'Listen,' said Declan, his carved face registering exasperation as well as impatience. 'There's a spring snowstorm out there the like of which I haven't seen in years. You have nowhere to sleep, and the Cambrian is the best of a bad job. What's to wait for? Or are you expecting young Lochinvar to arrive on his motorized steed again to whisk you out of my clutches?'

Kerry looked away. 'If you mean Larry, he's dead.'

Declan didn't reply at once. There was an awkward silence and then, once again, she felt his hand on her shoulder. 'I'm sorry,' he said curtly. 'I didn't know.'

'It's all right.'

24

There was another silence, longer this time, before Declan said, 'The baby. Is it — ?'

'I lost the baby. Soon after we married.'

'I see. I didn't know that, either.' He gave her shoulder a brief squeeze then drew his arm back stiffly. 'That must have been rough. I'm sorry.'

He meant it this time. She could tell from the way his voice had deepened. And suddenly the old sorrow, the feeling of emptiness, came back, and she found herself brushing away tears.

Declan pulled out a handkerchief, wiped her eyes efficiently, then put his arm around her and held her, giving brisk comfort as he had always done.

After a while Kerry said, 'I wanted that baby.' She gave him a watery smile. 'For all I don't know how in the world I'd have managed. I'll never forget him. Never ever. He was a boy, you know.' She swallowed. 'But — well, I've come to terms with losing him.' When she saw Declan eyeing her skeptically, she insisted, 'Really I have. There are times when I think it was meant to happen the way it did.'

'Perhaps,' Declan agreed bluntly. 'And no doubt . . . ' He broke off, obviously searching for words that wouldn't bring on more tears.

'You were going to say perhaps one day I'll have other children,' Kerry said bleakly. 'I suppose it's possible. If I ever decide to remarry.' She glanced at his face, grave, strong, unsentimental, and suddenly she heard herself saying, 'Larry left me a year after our wedding. I'm not in any hurry to try again.'

There. It was out in the open. She hadn't wanted to admit Larry's faithlessness to Declan. It had something to do with pride. But there didn't seem much point in trying to hide it. She had always had trouble hiding things from Declan. She studied the corded sinews in his neck. Funny, for a moment there it had been almost as if the boy she had adored as a child had come back to her, as patient and reassuring as ever. But that boy had been a man for a long time now. A hard, successful man, who had no time for childish prevarication.

And the past could never really be repeated.

Declan's face was unreadable. 'Aren't you?' he said. 'In a hurry? Then maybe there's hope for you yet.' He strode across to the counter and leaned heavily on the bell.

Now what did he mean by that? Kerry stared at the broad expanse of his back in a gray parka. Odd how he could make even a practical parka look like conventional corporate clothing. But there had always been something about Declan that exuded power. Not that she had ever known him to attempt to take advantage of his superior size and strength. Only once had she seen him bloody a nose, and that had been on her behalf, when a tourist heading for the falls had tried to lure her into his car on the pretext of needing directions. Declan had seen the man grab her wrist, and the next moment her attacker had been flat on his back on the sidewalk with Declan's hand at his throat.

Kerry was brought abruptly back to the present and her current predicament, when a middle-aged woman she had never seen before bustled in from the back blowing her nose.

'Sorry to keep you waiting,' the woman said. 'We've been so busy this evening I've hardly had time to catch my breath. The storm, you know. All the through traffic had to stop off for the night.' She beamed across the counter at Kerry. 'Oh, dear. *You're* not looking for a room, are you? We're full right up. Whole town's booked up, if what I've heard is right.'

Wonderful, thought Kerry. Now what?

But Declan was already solving the problem in his own unique and autocratic way.

'That's all right, Mrs. Kovalik,' she heard him explaining to the woman. 'Mrs. Simms is my sister. I guess she'll just have to bunk in with me. Can't have her spending the night in a snowbank, can we?' He gave the Cambrian's owner a smile that made her blush and make twittery little noises in her throat.

'No, of course not,' Mrs. Kovalik agreed. 'That will be perfectly all right, Mr. King. I'll just make a note of it in my book.'

'That's settled then,' said Declan, turning to Kerry with a look so bland it made her want to hit him. 'Come along, Sis.'

Kerry gasped. 'But,' she began. 'I can't — '

'Don't worry, you won't inconvenience me more than usual. Now, where did you leave your luggage?'

'It's . . . ' Oh. She didn't have any luggage. At least she did, but it was locked in her car. Which was on the sick list at Dieter's Garage. Probably just as well, too, because under no circumstances did she mean to share a room with Declan.

'It doesn't matter,' she said quickly. 'Declan, I won't be staying. I've decided to — um — catch the late bus out of town.' She shivered suddenly as melted snow trickled down her neck.

'Can't,' said Mrs. Kovalik succinctly. 'Canceled.'

'Oh.' Kerry swallowed and glanced helplessly at Declan.

He gave her a smile that was all cool mastery and malice, and nodded at the stairs leading up to the rooms. 'That way,' he said to Kerry, before turning to thank Mrs. Kovalik for her help.

When Kerry didn't move, he gave a sigh of exasperation, took two strides across the lobby and, taking her by the elbow, practically ran her up the stairs.

'For heaven's sake, don't make us look like a couple of teenagers on a naughty weekend,' he said coldly.

'She'll guess I'm not your sister anyway,' protested Kerry.

'Of course she will. If not tonight, then tomorrow, once the tongues have had a chance to wag.'

30

'So what's the point — '

'The point, my dear little sister, is that the proprieties will have been seen to be observed. As long as Mrs. K. can plead ignorance, she'll be more than happy to receive payment for your bed.' He stopped to unlock a door. 'In here.'

Kerry found herself standing in a clean, functional-looking room with a brown carpet, brown curtains, two straight-backed brown chairs — and two beds.

Her shoulders sagged with relief.

Declan eyed her sardonically. 'Don't tell me you're still reading those ridiculous books.'

'What's that supposed to mean?'

'That old cliché about the virtuous heroine being forced to spend a night in the villainous hero's bed. That's what you were expecting, isn't it? Rarely happens in real life though.' He cast a disparaging glance at her slim figure in the bulky parka, and added, 'Fortunately.'

'Is that so?' retorted Kerry, surprised

to find his look hurt. 'Then can I assume, since you seem to know so much about them, that you also enjoy slumming in those books? Which, by the way, make a lot more sense than that mayhem and murder stuff you were always reading.'

Declan was not at all put out. '*Touché*. And yes, I have to admit, I did occasionally take it upon myself to supervise your reading.'

'Pompous ass,' said Kerry unoriginally.

He inclined his head. 'Thank you. But may I remind you that there was a time when you were more than willing to put up with my pomposity? Welcomed it as a lifeline, in fact.'

Kerry kicked off her boots and sat down suddenly on the nearest bed. 'Oh, Declan. I *am* sorry. It *was* awful of me.'

'It was, wasn't it? But quite in character.' He unzipped his parka. 'And I suppose behaving as if I'm the carrier of some kind of unpleasantly modern disease — or at the very least, a seducer of innocent ex-virgins — is your way of making it up to me. Is that it?'

'Oh, Declan,' said Kerry again. 'I didn't mean — '

'No,' said Declan. 'You never do. That's always been your trouble, hasn't it, Kerry? Leap first, look afterward, and leave me to pick up the pieces.' He threw off the parka and sat on the other bed to remove his boots. Then he flung himself back on the pillows and linked his hands under his head. 'But you're a big girl now, aren't you, sweetheart? Too big to spank, too old to make excuses for. So perhaps you had better accept the current situation . . . ' He waved at the two single beds. 'As your best option under awkward circumstances. And you might *try* not to think of me as an apprentice Jack the Ripper. I have never, to my knowledge, done you the slightest harm, even when sorely tempted and eminently justified, and I find the suggestion that I might quite unflattering. And damned irritating. Besides . . . ' He propped himself up on one elbow. 'If you could see yourself now, you'd realize that even if I'd become a raving sex maniac since last we met, I'd be giving the matter serious second thoughts.'

Kerry stopped scowling and blinked. 'What? What's the matter with me?'

His only answer was a slanted, thoroughly aggravating smile.

She got up and went to look in the big mirror above the dresser.

Declan was right. Her oval face was totally devoid of makeup, and except for a smudge of green eyeshadow across one cheek, her complexion was more faded lily than Canadian rose. Her eyes were washed-out mauve saucers, and her long blond hair drooped damply around her shoulders like honey that has sat in the cupboard for too long. Her blue parka was wet and crusted with snow, making her look like an underfed waif instead of the slim young woman she knew she was.

'Oh, dear,' she said, tugging at her zipper and throwing a wry glance at

34

Declan, who looked amazingly sexy in his heavy sweater and damp jeans. Still corporate, but definitely sexy. But then he had always been a seductive specimen of manhood. She had been resentfully conscious of his magnetism even in the days when he had appointed himself her guardian, overseer and censorious wet blanket. His virility had scared her in a way, perhaps even driven her into Larry's irresponsible, fun-loving arms at a time when she was desperately searching for affection.

Declan had cared for her, too, of course. But his repressive interference when she misbehaved wasn't the kind of caring calculated to appeal to a rebellious, high-spirited young girl who had just discovered the intoxicating influence of hormones.

She watched him run a quick, derisive glance over her damp body in pink sweater and jeans. 'Not your average sex maniac's preferred fare, I'm afraid,' he murmured.

'Since when have you ever been average?' scoffed Kerry, marching into the bathroom to toss her soggy parka into the bath.

Declan lifted an eyebrow. 'A compliment?' he asked when she came back. 'Or was that your oblique way of telling me I compare unfavorably with your standard line in roommates?'

'Oh, Declan.' Kerry shook her head and padded across the room to stare out of the window at the storm. 'I don't have a standard line in roommates. I haven't had a roommate in six years.'

'Haven't you? My name isn't, 'Oh, Declan,' by the way.' He paused, and when he spoke again his voice was clipped, less flippant. 'What happened, Kerry?'

'It doesn't — it's not . . . '

'Not my business? Think again, sweetheart. I may not have been heartbroken to have you taken off my hands, but neither did I appreciate being made to look like a fool by a randy little jerk in black leather. With painted-on tattoos. You owe me one, Mrs. Simms.'

Kerry spun around and stood with her back against the window. 'I took my old name back,' she said. 'I'm Kerry Fleming. How did you know about Larry's tattoos?'

Declan shifted a shoulder against the pillows. 'Larry Simms may have had redeeming qualities. I hope he had. But he would never have had the guts to go through with genuine pain.'

Kerry sighed. 'You're right, of course.'

'I know.' Declan sat up and swung his feet to the floor. 'I asked you what happened, Kerry.'

Kerry eyed him doubtfully. She didn't want to tell him what a terrible mistake she had made. But she had a feeling he already suspected. And she did owe him. There had never been any doubt about that. If she'd thought for one moment that he had seriously wanted to marry her, she wouldn't have acted like the heroine of bad melodrama and fallen naïvely into Larry's conniving arms.

She had been crazy about Larry. But in the end it was Declan, six years older and by that time amassing a fortune in Toronto and New York, who had been there in her hour of desperate need. With grim resignation he had dried her frantic tears, for once not telling her she ought to know better — better than to get herself pregnant by a man who said he was sorry, but he just wasn't ready to be a father so she would have to handle the problem on her own. Larry had written her a check, which she had promptly and impractically torn up, and right after that he had left town.

'Kerry,' said Declan, breaking into her thoughts and rising to his feet with an agility and abruptness that made her jump. 'I asked you a question. I mean to have an answer.'

He began to advance across the room. Automatically she glanced behind her for escape.

'It's a long drop,' Declan said pointedly. 'I don't advise it.'

Kerry swallowed and put her hands behind her to grip the sill. 'Does it matter?' she asked him. 'What have the sordid details of my marriage to do with you? And anyway, why should you care?'

'Because, as you pointed out, I allowed you to marry Larry Simms. At the time it seemed to me that as the father of your child he had the right. And the responsibility. I also believed he cared for you and wanted to make amends. And presumably you loved him, or thought you did.' He pushed a hand through his hair, which promptly fell back into place, and went on in a resigned but marginally less abrasive tone. 'I'd no particular wish to make you suffer, Kerry. But I'm beginning to get the idea you'd have been better off suffering at my hands than at Larry's.'

'Would I have suffered?' Kerry frowned, not understanding. 'If I'd married you, I mean?'

'Probably. You were ridiculously young. And in adult circles I've never been known for my patience.'

She gave a short, brittle laugh. 'Just as well then, isn't it, that you didn't try to hold me to my promise?'

'No doubt,' Declan said drily. 'Nevertheless I do have a stake in knowing the outcome of my withdrawal from the marital arena. It has something to do with conscience, I suppose. I do have one.' He took a step toward her and then stopped, frowning slightly. 'News of Carmody Falls dried up after I bought my parents the house they wanted in Minneapolis. But in the beginning I heard you and Larry were getting along quite well.'

Yes, his family would have thought that. They had been her own parents' greatest friends and fellow card addicts, and had usually been too absorbed in their obsession with bridge to take much interest in what went on around them. It was their families' obsessive card-playing that had thrown Kerry and Declan together in the first place in spite of the difference in their ages.

They had both grown up conscious that they were frequently regarded by their respective parents as no more than annoying distractions from the much more important business of duplicate bridge.

Declan, though, had always had a mental toughness about him that had enabled him to laugh off his parents' unthinking neglect. They were his family, and he accepted them as they were. But he had sympathized with the anxious little girl who lacked his natural instinct for survival, and had tried to give her the security and confidence she needed. And for as long as she had remained a worshipful and adoring child, their relationship had been one of mutual affection. Then in her teen years, all that had changed.

'Kerry?' said Declan. 'Stop dreaming.'

She started. 'I wasn't — I mean, did you say something?'

'You know I did.'

She made a conscious effort not to

shuffle her feet or drop her eyes. 'You really want to know about me and Larry?' she said.

'I wouldn't have asked if I didn't. Believe it or not, Kerry, I have occasionally wondered how you were and what you were doing. Please enlighten me.'

He was standing a foot away from her now, with his legs apart and his thumbs hooked into a wide, Western-style belt. And it was almost as if the last seven years of her life had never happened. Almost. But not quite. Declan still took it as his right to give her orders. That was nothing new. But something had changed. He seemed taller, even more explicitly male, and she was aware of him as she had never allowed herself to be aware of her old friend and protector. In the old days when she had felt her stomach curl the moment he walked into a room, she had put it firmly down to indigestion.

She didn't have indigestion now.

'Well?' he said in that exacting way

she remembered so well, making her feel like a ten-year-old again. A ten-year-old who has slipped out after dark while her parents are defeating a grand slam — and been summarily hauled home again by Declan.

She cleared her throat and brushed a strand of wet hair out of her eyes.

Declan, who was looking more formidable as each second passed, gestured at one of the straight-backed chairs. 'You'd better sit down,' he said. 'I'm assuming this is going to take more than a couple of minutes.'

He didn't move, but Kerry edged her way around him and sat down. For some reason her legs were being annoyingly unsupportive, and sitting seemed a sensible thing to do.

'Good girl.' Declan nodded approvingly, and took over her place by the window. She wished he hadn't, because the neon lights on the shop across the road created a flaming aura around his head. It made him look dangerous, devilish and not at all like the Declan

43

she thought she knew.

He waited, silently, for her to speak. Which, after a long while, she did.

'Larry only married me because his uncle found out I was pregnant,' she said woodenly.

Declan frowned. 'I'm not a fool, Kerry. People rarely marry to please their uncles.'

Kerry closed her eyes. 'They do when the uncle has a lot of money. And old-fashioned standards.'

'The two don't necessarily go together. Rather the opposite, in fact.'

She felt like saying, 'You should know, Mr. High Finance,' but she bit her tongue instead. 'Larry's Uncle Charles said he'd disinherit him if he didn't make an honest woman of me,' she explained wearily, surprised to find that such an ancient wound was still capable of causing her pain. 'He was an old man — a great-uncle, really — so Larry decided to make the best of a bad job and marry me.'

Declan's lip curled down. 'Yes, I can

see why he might have thought of it in those terms. Having been there myself.'

Kerry put her knees together and sat up very straight. 'What terms?'

'I was talking about making the best of a bad job.'

'It *wasn't* your job,' she said stiffly. 'There was no reason for you to put yourself out if you didn't want to.'

'True. But keeping you out of trouble had become a habit. Naturally I came home when I got your letter.'

'To marry me?' she asked, not quite believing it.

'That wasn't my intention. But in the end it seemed the best thing to do.'

'Why?'

'I told you. Habit. A certain relish for a challenge, which you were — and for some reason, which at present escapes me, I believe I was fond of you at the time.' He paused, eyes gleaming with an amusement that infuriated Kerry.

'That's it?' she said. 'For that you were willing to take on another man's child?'

'No.' He paused, and when he spoke again his tone was harder, no longer even faintly mocking. 'Not just for that. There was also the small matter of my charming cousin, Oliver. The Kings owed you for the behavior of that young snake in worm's clothing, Kerry.'

Kerry pulled on the sleeve of her pink sweater. He sounded as if he were talking about the payment of a ten dollar debt instead of a lifetime commitment. But it wasn't altogether out of character. Declan had always taken responsibility for his family's shortcomings — usually with a tolerant affection born of years of enforced independence.

He hadn't been tolerant about his cousin.

'I don't want to talk about Oliver,' Kerry said.

'Neither do I. I want to talk about what happened to you after Larry elected to make the best of a bad job.'

Kerry met his eyes briefly then looked away. 'I'm not really sure,' she said slowly. 'I think he did care for me in a way. At least at first. But he felt he'd been pushed into marriage, and he resented that. Besides, I have an idea he was one of those men who love the chase but lose interest once they've captured the prize.'

'Prize, be damned,' muttered Declan. 'Capturing you must have been about as challenging as capturing Bambi.'

This time Kerry, nettled, did say, 'You should know.'

'That,' said Declan, 'is rank ingratitude. You were never on my list of seasonal prey.'

It was true. He had never pursued her. But there was a kind of coiled tension about him now that puzzled her, made her wary of provoking his wrath.

'I'm not ungrateful,' she said quickly.

'Good.' He waited, eyebrows raised.

Kerry swallowed. 'Larry thought I was fun when we first started going out together,' she explained, anxious now to get through the rest of her sad little tale without giving away to Declan how desperately alone and helpless she had felt when Larry had *stopped* thinking she was fun. For some reason, she didn't want her old mentor to think of her as helpless.

'When I lost the baby shortly after we were married,' she hurried on, 'Larry — well, I was depressed for a while, and he found that very dull. He didn't understand depression. Especially as he'd never really wanted the child he felt was the cause of his being tricked into marriage.'

She was staring straight ahead as she spoke. There was a picture of a bluebird above her bed, and the wind was blowing snow against the window. Then, from the corner of her eye, she saw Declan make a quick, impatient movement.

She looked up.

'Larry Simms wasn't tricked,' he rasped. 'In my opinion, Larry Simms got exactly what he deserved.'

Kerry wrapped her arms around her chest and tried to draw back into the unwelcoming arms of the hard chair. 'Thank you,' she said, forcing all inflection from her voice. 'I suppose he did, didn't he? He got me.'

'Kerry,' said Declan, after a pause during which she heard him take a deep breath, hold it, then let it out again very slowly. 'Do you have any idea what you're doing?'

Kerry cradled her arms further around her chest, seeking a security that had evaporated only seconds after she had first laid eyes on Declan in Phil's café. 'No,' she said. 'What?'

'You are making me want to commit grievous bodily harm on a honey blonde.'

'Why?' she asked, hurt, but knowing he wouldn't do it.

Declan shrugged. 'I'm not sure. Something to do with the scared-little-girl routine, I suppose. It brings out the worst in me.'

'I'm not scared,' Kerry said, shifting to the edge of her chair just in case. She uncradled her arms. 'And I'm certainly not a little girl.'

'No?' He paused to give her slim, woman's figure a brisk appraisal. 'No, I see you're not in the most obvious sense. But don't twist my words on me, Kerry. I had about all I could take of that the last time 'round. What I meant when I said Larry got what he deserved was that a man who denies responsibility for his child, and then changes his mind for the sake of an inheritance, isn't worth a whole lot of sympathy. Now . . . ' He pulled the other chair across the room, swung it around and sat astride it with his arms crossed loosely on the back. 'Let's hear the rest of it. Then we'll go get you something to eat.'

Oh. Kerry blinked, uncomfortably conscious that his right knee was almost touching her left one. At least he'd remembered she hadn't eaten. But of course Declan didn't forget things that mattered. In fact Declan just didn't forget things. It was one of his most irritating traits.

'The rest of it,' she said, anxious to

50

finish her story now, 'is that Larry was all chuckles and charm when we were going out together. Like a happy-go-lucky kid. But once I got pregnant, things changed. He married me for his uncle's money, but he'd never really wanted a wife. Then I lost the baby and he lost his job at the mill after turning up late with a hangover once too often — and life wasn't a game for him anymore.'

'Or for you, either, I imagine. Must have been something of a shock.'

Kerry eyed him doubtfully. Was that compassion, or a guarded satisfaction she heard behind the dryly spoken words? Or merely indifference? When he returned her look with a neutrality that gave nothing away, Kerry sighed and returned her gaze to the oblivious bluebird.

'Or for me, either,' she agreed. 'But by that time I was getting used to shocks. So Larry blustered and grumbled and whined, and I got a job as a waitress. Then one night he took off on his motorcycle. He didn't come back.'

'Unusually thoughtful of him,' drawled Declan. 'Do you mean to tell me he found marriage to you such a burden that he gave up his inheritance to get out of it?'

Kerry gaped at him in glazed disbelief. How could he? How could he speak to her like that? She had told him much more than she'd meant to, and now, instead of the patronizing sympathy she had half expected, he was making *jokes*. Cynical, inappropriate jokes.

'That's not funny,' she snapped. Except it was, in a warped sort of way. She smiled frostily. 'No, Larry didn't give up his inheritance. He'd already lost it. Uncle Charles changed his mind and left it all to me on the condition that Larry wasn't to see a penny of it. When Larry found out, we had a terrible fight. Right after that he left me.'

'It didn't occur to him that a will like

that would be simple enough to break? With your co-operation, of course.'

Kerry studied the wide leather band of Declan's wristwatch. 'Yes, it occurred to him. But I wasn't very cooperative by then. And Uncle Charles looked set to stay alive as long as he could, just so he could keep things stirred up. I expect Larry planned to come back to me the moment his uncle died. But he didn't get the chance, because four years ago he drove his bike into a ditch and broke his neck.'

'Another piece of good management,' murmured Declan. He smoothed a hand over his jaw. 'The man did have his moments.'

Kerry gasped and put a hand to her face as if he'd slapped her.

'Larry was my husband,' she said.

3

A door slammed somewhere down the hall. Mrs. Kovalik's voice drifted up the stairs discussing sheets — and Kerry, her eyes riveted on Declan's, started to rise from her chair.

He put out a hand and gently pushed her back. 'No,' he said. 'There's no need to act as if I've stabbed you to the heart. I know Larry was your husband. But I'm damned if I'm going to pretend to mourn him. You needn't either, around me. Because I won't believe you.'

'Maybe you won't,' said Kerry, thinking how much harsher and more defined the angles of his face had become in the years since she had last set eyes on him. 'But the fact is I *did* mourn Larry. How could I not mourn a failed marriage and the man I once thought I loved? Grandfather and

Mother were gone by then, as well. It wasn't that I wanted Larry back exactly, but I did feel very — alone.' She turned her head away, so Declan wouldn't see how much the memories hurt.

'Hmm.' Declan was unmoved. 'Poor Little Orphan Kerry with the nice inheritance.'

'What?' She swung around, startled and enraged. How dare he imply that she was only pretending she had cared about her husband?

Declan, eyebrows slightly lifted, gazed back at her with a thin, carved smile on his lips.

After a few seconds, Kerry dropped her eyes. Had he deliberately set out to make her angry? Or was his lack of sympathy intended to snap her out of her moment of self-pity? If so, it worked.

'I didn't *poison* Larry. Or Uncle Charles,' she said, surprised to discover how calm she suddenly felt. 'So I wish you'd stop looking at me as if you suspect me of cooking up newts and blindworms in that rusty old stewpot Mother left me.'

The carved smile was replaced by genuine amusement. 'More likely burnt scrambled eggs. Your cooking never was up to much.'

Kerry curled her fingers into fists. She was *not* going to let him get to her. 'How would you know? By the time I learned to cook, you were off in Toronto turning your tiddledywinks into a fortune.'

'Monopoly,' he corrected her. 'I only play tiddledy winks with other people's fortunes. And in case you've forgotten, I returned to Carmody Falls often enough to bail you out of trouble. On the last occasion the bailout would have been rather permanent, as I remember.'

'Do you *have* to keep bringing that up?' Kerry demanded. 'I know I shouldn't have abandoned you for Larry. But I didn't *ask* you to marry me, Declan. I didn't even *want* you to marry me. And what's more, you know you were relieved when I chose Larry instead.'

'Mmm. I was, in a way. But having made up my mind to take you on, losing you to Young Lochinvar in Black Leather was something of a blow to my self-esteem.' He extended his legs on either side of her chair and his right knee brushed against her thigh.

Kerry gulped. His low, chocolate-velvet voice was smooth and serious, but there was a wry, self-mocking slant to his lips that made her wonder if he thought the whole subject of their unfinished wedding was a joke.

'Your ego doesn't look even remotely bruised to me,' she said, pressing her knees primly together.

He laughed. 'Doesn't it? I wonder why that is?'

She didn't answer. He knew very well why. If Declan had bruises he never let them show. And just because *he* had shrugged off unthinking parental neglect to become a self-reliant, hardheaded man who only broke rules for a profit, didn't mean he had had a right to expect the same tough resilience of her.

He had expected just that though. She stared at the dun-colored carpet, so like the one in the house she had grown up in, and remembered how he had reacted when she'd started to fight back against what she had mistakenly perceived as her parents' indifference. As a teenager, she had worn wild, dramatic clothing, instigated wild, dramatic parties intended to shock, taken up smoking, and only stopped just short of attracting attention from the police.

Declan, furious and impatient with her antics, had done his best to set her on a more productive path. And after a while, instead of seeing him as a friend, she had begun to think of him as an autocratic spoilsport.

Yet in her hour of need, it had never occurred to her to turn to anyone but Declan.

When she told him about Larry and the baby, he had sworn with, for him, extraordinary vehemence, and said that he'd better marry her himself.

'It's the only way to keep you out of trouble,' he had snapped when she'd tried to protest. 'Because if you think any wife of mine is going to get away with the kind of nonsense this town has been putting up with from you, you're very much mistaken.'

She hadn't doubted him. And she hadn't wanted to marry him, either. But her father was dead, and the family doctor said her ailing mother should on no account be burdened with the worry of a pregnant and unmarried daughter. Her grandfather had enough trouble coping with the problems of old age. And, most important of all, there was a baby to consider.

In the end, Kerry's childhood habit of doing as Declan told her had won out, and she had reluctantly and a little guiltily agreed to a marriage which she knew would be more to her advantage than to his.

'What's this?' Declan's deep voice

interrupted her reminiscences.

Kerry blinked. He was holding her hand. But when she looked, she discovered he was only uncurling the fingers she hadn't known she'd clenched into a fist.

'Thinking of bruising more than my ego?' he asked. 'I won't let you, you know. Although I do seem to remember you once tried to punch me on the nose.'

'Only because you had your arms clamped around my waist and were shoving me under a cold shower,' Kerry protested.

Funny, she was feeling a surprisingly urgent need for a cold shower right this minute. Declan's touch was sending the most shockingly fiery message up her arm.

'And a well-deserved dunking it would have been,' he said amiably. 'Hadn't you just attempted to break into the school and spray-paint the walls with words you had no business knowing?'

'No,' said Kerry. 'That wasn't me. That was Larry.'

'Ah. Then it must have been the time you decided to play Scottish marching tunes at three o'clock in the morning — using the neighborhood garbage cans for drums.'

'Cymbals,' Kerry corrected him. 'I played the lids.'

'Don't split hairs. You were a public menace and you know it.'

Kerry raised wary eyes to his face. The words were stern, disapproving as usual. But was that a quiver she saw teasing the edge of his mouth?

'Yes.' She had to agree with him. 'I suppose I was. Except when *you* turned up to interfere.' She decided she must have imagined the quiver, and added firmly, 'But I'm not like that anymore.'

'Aren't you?' Declan was noncommittal.

He was still holding her hand, and she pulled it away so quickly that her nails scraped across his palm, which, surprisingly, was much lighter than the tough brown back of his hand. Odd how this man who had achieved success in fluorescent-lit boardrooms managed to look as though he spent his days sweating beneath the sun.

'Claws sharp as ever, I see,' he murmured, inspecting her pinkly polished nails.

Why did she have the feeling something other than her nails was absorbing his attention and causing him to frown? 'It was an accident,' she said stiffly. 'I'm sorry.'

'Of course.' He stood up and swung his chair back as if he were brushing off a cobweb. Then he turned and held out his hand. 'Up you get. Time to get over to Phil's before he decides to close up and go home. I don't know about you, but I can think of better ways to spend my evening than driving around town in a snowstorm in search of food.'

'No reason why you should. I'm quite capable of looking after myself.'

He ignored that and said, 'Where's your jacket?'

Kerry glared. 'In the bath.'

'Right.' He strode across the room, and a moment later she heard a muffled oath coming from the bathroom.

'I thought you said you could look after yourself,' he said, emerging almost at once with her parka swinging from his fingers. The crusted snow had melted, and it was wringing wet. 'This thing's about as waterproof as lace.'

'I didn't expect snow. And I was driving, so it didn't matter.'

'I see. So where's your car? And your luggage?'

Kerry sighed. She had known she would have to explain about her luggage sooner or later. She'd hoped for later. Declan already thought her brain was missing a few crucial connectors. Now his opinion would only be confirmed.

'My car's at Dieter's Garage,' she told him, trying to sound casual, and suspecting she sounded sullen instead. 'My luggage is in it.'

His eyebrows lifted a fraction. 'Then

we'd better fetch it.'

'We can't. Dieter's gone to a party. The garage is locked.'

The eyebrows continued to travel upward. 'You're sure?'

'Oh, yes. He told me he was closing at five. I meant to borrow Lori's car to pick up my things, but what with the snowstorm, and the chicken pox — '

'I know,' said Declan heavily. 'You forgot. Surprise, surprise.' He threw her parka back into the bath. 'What's wrong with your car?'

'The break pads are shot. Dieter had to phone for replacements.'

'For break pads? What in hell kind of a car do you drive?'

'A Saab. It's Swedish.'

'I know it's Swedish.'

She could see him thinking, Trust Kerry to buy something exotic that small towns aren't likely to have parts for.

'It's a very good car,' she said defensively.

'I agree. So is there some reason you

64

didn't get it checked over before you left wherever you came from?'

'Winnipeg. And I was in a hurry.'

Now he was thinking, You would be. It was written all over his face.

'There's only one thing for it then,' said Declan after a moment's pause during which Kerry did indeed contemplate bruising his superior nose. 'I'll get Phil to pack some takeout while you stay here and reflect upon your sins.'

Kerry pressed her lips together, having come to the reluctant conclusion that if she hoped to eat tonight, there was no sense provoking Declan to retaliate. He was quite capable of sitting back and informing her that going without supper would do her good. And one didn't brave Northern Ontario winters — or in this case inclement springs — in a jacket that without the heat of her body to keep it warm was by now not only damp, but icy.

'What sins?' she asked finally, unable to maintain the discreet silence she knew was advisable.

'The usual ones. Sheer carelessness and irresponsibility.'

Kerry looked over her shoulder for something to throw. Then she remembered she was twenty-five years old and that there was no need to allow Declan's inflammatory presence to arouse all the old childish instincts that hadn't surfaced in years.

'There's the lamp,' he said softly. 'But I promise you if you try it, you'll pay.'

He knew her too well. She turned back to face him, and discovered he was lounging against the wall with his hands in the pockets of his jeans. But it was his eyes that drew her attention. They were examining her in a way that totally confused her. If they hadn't been Declan's eyes, she would have sworn they were calmly stripping off her clothes. Was *that* how he meant her to pay? The thought sent a not altogether unpleasant shiver down her spine.

But of course they *were* Declan's eyes, and they finished whatever they were doing with unhurried efficiency before he detached himself from the wall and went to collect his parka from the bed. As he bent to pick it up, Kerry took in for the first time how appealing he looked from that particular angle, and tipped her head to one side for a better view. She pinched her lips together. Yes, a remarkably attractive male backside considering it belonged to such a sober and impossibly dictatorial man. She lifted her hand, then remembered who he was and dropped it quickly.

Not quickly enough.

Declan's eyes narrowed, and he said in a voice that was both a provocation and a challenge, 'Why don't you try it?'

His gaze dropped to her hips, and she gulped and said quickly, 'No, thank you. I don't do corporations.'

His head jerked up, and for an instant she thought she'd gone too far, as astonishment chased disbelief and then outrage across his face. But after a moment his lips parted in a smile that made her catch her breath. 'Is that so?'

he said softly. 'Then we'll have to find out just exactly what it is you do do. Won't we? But I think you'd better eat first. You were always more compliant on a full stomach.'

He shrugged on his parka, and was through the door before Kerry had time to come up with a retort.

Now what had that been about? Her empty stomach knotted suddenly, and she wandered over to the window to watch the reflection of the store lights shimmering like fire across the snow. There was a regular blizzard out there now. The wind had come up and chased the snowflakes into great drifts that were piling up along the sides of the road.

She pressed her head against the glass. What *did* Declan have in mind for her? Curiously, and in spite of his enigmatic words, she wasn't frightened. She might be trapped in this bedroom with a man who had become almost a stranger, but she was sure — well, almost sure — that he wouldn't touch her without her permission. Not after what his cousin had tried to do.

Funny, she rarely thought about that incident any more, although at the tender age of sixteen, after her adoring relationship with Declan had begun to change, she had fallen for Oliver like a witless shooting star.

Sent from Vancouver to spend the summer with his aunt and uncle, Oliver King had looked like a younger and softer version of Declan. When he told Kerry he loved her and wanted to marry her, she accepted his word without question — until the night she rounded a corner near the bowling alley and saw him kissing Loralee Smith, who had a reputation for being generous with her favors.

Kerry rested both hands on the window. It felt cold and damp. Lord, how devastated she'd been. How she had screamed at Oliver, shouted and called him names until Loralee, routed, had fled the scene.

What followed had been even worse.

Deprived of his night of lust, Oliver had lost his temper and backed Kerry up against the bowling alley wall. By the time she was able to tear herself away after biting him hard on the lip, he had ripped the front of her blouse and was busy unfastening her skirt.

Kerry, tripping and stumbling for the safety of her home, had run smack into Declan who was walking Maybelle Jensen home from the movies.

Her parents had been away at a bridge tournament, and Declan had spent hours comforting her, trying to convince her that her world hadn't come to an end just because Oliver had destroyed her adolescent dreams. When he left, he promised her that his contemptible cousin would be on his way out of town within the hour.

He had kept his promise. She had never seen Oliver again, and a few months later, still looking for love and acceptance, she had fallen in with Larry and his friends. Within the year she had become Larry's girl.

But she wasn't anyone's girl now, and although the old high-handedness was still as much in evidence as ever, in the seven years since she had last seen Declan, he had become an incredibly disturbing and exciting man.

She wished very much that he hadn't turned up again at this particular moment in her life.

It had taken her a long time to recover from her ill-fated marriage to Larry. She could do without Declan around to stir up old memories and forgotten feelings — reminding her that at the age of eighteen she had been Carmody Falls' biggest fool.

Or maybe not. She might have married Declan. Which could have been an even bigger mistake.

Why, oh why, had he chosen this weekend, of all weekends, to come back here . . . ?

When Declan backed through the door fifteen minutes later, carrying several foil containers and a bottle of Chianti, Kerry asked at once, 'Declan, what are you doing here? Why did you come back to Carmody Falls?'

'Is there some reason I shouldn't visit the town where I grew up?' He pushed the door shut with his hip.

She realized her question had probably sounded rude. 'No, of course not. But your parents aren't here any longer. Don't you plan to spend Easter with them?'

'No. They're the bridge pros for a cruise line at present. Somewhere in the Caribbean.' He laid the foil containers on the dresser. 'We see each other when our respective schedules permit.'

In other words, nothing had changed there.

Declan opened the containers. 'Help yourself.' He made it sound like an order.

Kerry needed no encouragement. She was starving. She hurried across the room and began to heap food onto a paper plate.

Declan had managed to acquire a selection of pastas and a salad that looked as though it had seen crisper days. 'Phil's specialty,' he said from behind her. 'Leftovers. He was just closing.'

'You mean you couldn't throw your weight around and bully him into making something fresh?' Now why had she said that? The leftovers smelled delicious.

'I don't bully. Any more than I allow others to bully me,' Declan replied pointedly. 'Nor would I dream of asking Phil to work overtime on behalf of a spoiled young woman who could perfectly well have eaten while he was open.'

'No, of course not,' said Kerry quickly. 'It was a silly thing to say. I'm not spoiled, and I wouldn't dream of asking, either.' She sat down on the nearest chair and began to eat.

Declan, who was busy with the bottle of wine, said, 'I'm glad to hear it.'

She looked up sharply. Didn't he believe her? Did he really think she was so inconsiderate as to expect a busy restauranteur to work late for her express convenience? Damn him, he still had the power to make her squirm — even when she had nothing to squirm about.

The cork gave a soft pop, and he poured wine into two tumblers and handed one to her. She saw that it was an exceptionally good vintage.

'To chance meetings,' said Declan, holding up his glass and smiling his disturbingly lopsided smile.

'Yes,' said Kerry, who wasn't sure there was anything to celebrate about a chance meeting that had forced her into such close proximity with Declan. She wished he would sit down. His heroic frame seemed to dominate the room, making her feel small and insignificant. She lifted her glass. 'To old friends. Declan, what *are* you doing here?'

'I'd have thought that was obvious. I'm providing you with shelter from the storm. For which piece of misguided altruism you have so far shown very little gratitude. However, the night is still young.'

Kerry swallowed a portion of pasta and choked. 'I'm grateful. But not *that* grateful,' she exclaimed.

'No? How grateful are you?'

The light from the window was making him look devilish again, and Kerry took a quick sip of wine and blurted, 'You said you weren't an apprentice Jack the Ripper.'

'I'm not.' The corner of his lip curled wickedly. 'My sexual appetites run along considerably more conventional lines — '

'I'm not interested in your sexual appetites,' said Kerry quickly. That smile of his was stirring up sensations she hadn't felt in years. 'Declan, why won't you tell me why you're here?'

He shrugged dismissively, and she had a feeling he would have preferred not to answer. 'It's no secret. Not any longer, thanks to Maybelle Jensen. I'm here for the official opening of the new arena.'

'You're what?' Kerry blinked. Surely he was having her on.

'You heard me.'

'Yes, but — Declan, you haven't driven all the way from Toronto just for the opening of a small-town arena.'

'No. I flew as far as Thunder Bay and drove from there.'

'But — why? It's not like you. You haven't lived here for years.'

He turned his back on her and went to stare out of the window. 'Because I couldn't avoid it. Not without displaying inexcusable arrogance and upsetting a number of good and decent people.'

'That's never bothered you before.' Only Declan could make 'good and decent' sound like 'interfering and inconvenient.'

His shoulders stiffened. 'It certainly wouldn't bother me to upset you,' he agreed flatly. 'However, if you must know, and since I've no doubt everyone else does by now — I bankrolled the complex.' He spun around and gave Kerry a hard stare, as if daring her to disbelieve him. When she only stared back, dumbfounded, he added curtly, 'The Town Council, in the person of my good friend Phil, approached me about it some time ago. I agreed, on condition that my involvement be kept quiet. Unfortunately that's not the way it happened.'

'Oh.' Kerry shook her head. Declan looked terribly grim. And something didn't add up. 'Isn't this an odd time of year to open a skating rink?' she asked, settling on the least contentious of her doubts.

'Not really. They've been using it since last fall, but the Council voted to hold off the official ceremonies until spring — when the weather was expected to be warmer.' He made an ironic gesture at the snow spattering softly against the window.

Kerry frowned. 'I see. Well it was generous of you, but — '

'It wasn't particularly generous. It's a tax write-off.'

Ah. Kerry nodded. Yes, that sounded

more like the Declan she knew. He was entirely comfortable with his wealth, but had never been good at accepting accolades for his philanthropic ventures. He almost seemed to resent being thanked. So it was entirely in character for him to want his involvement kept anonymous. But that didn't explain what had drawn him back to town. She would have expected him to stay away and send a minion to enjoy the limelight.

'I'm surprised you came, just the same,' she said bluntly.

'Are you? So am I. Believe me, I had no intention of showing up, until I heard from ... ' He stopped and pushed his hands into his pockets. 'From several of the councillors — that I was to be the guest of honor. And that the good people of Carmody Falls would be insulted if I didn't show my face.'

Yes, that made sense. Declan was arrogant, but she had never known him to inflict hurt on the undeserving.

'So that changed your mind,' she said, nodding her understanding.

'Mmm. You could say it did. Especially once I learned from Phil that Council planned to send Maybelle Jensen to Toronto to persuade me.' There was a miniscule smile on his lips, and his voice was drier than a desert.

Kerry put her glass down hastily. 'Maybelle Jensen? She's still in town?'

'Very much so. She's on the Council along with Phil. Quentin O'Malley is Mayor.'

'Oh,' said Kerry, as the light dawned. '*That's* how your secret got out. Maybelle wanted you to come, so she let the cat out of the bag.'

Declan shrugged and answered indirectly. 'Once the news was out and the rink named after me, the die was more or less cast.'

Kerry felt a sudden dryness in her throat. Pretty, manipulative Maybelle . . . She always had known how to get what she wanted. Except when she had wanted Declan. But that was a long time ago.

Things changed . . .

'So the chance to see Maybelle was the real reason you came back?' she taunted, keeping her tone light even though, oddly, the thought of Maybelle and Declan together made all her muscles tighten up.

'No. I came back for precisely the reason I gave you.'

Kerry gave a short, brittle laugh. 'Sure you can spare the time?'

'I've learned to make time when I need to,' he said coolly. 'It shouldn't cut too badly into my schedule. The Opening's on Monday, I'll be back in the office by Wednesday.'

Kerry smiled skeptically. He hadn't added that since Maybelle was still willing and available, she would fit nicely into his schedule, as well. But it was probably what he was thinking.

Declan had only taken the chocolate-box blonde out a few times in the old days, but he couldn't have been oblivious to her slightly too obvious charms. Not when they were offered so eagerly.

'So you *won't* be seeing Maybelle?' she asked, raising her eyebrows and hoping she sounded teasingly amused.

Declan smiled with a certain malevolence and came to sit on the nearest bed. 'Oh, I'll see her,' he said. 'As a Councillor, she'll be at the Opening.' He tilted his head and surveyed her with a cool, assessing gaze. 'You know, Miss Fleming, now that you've dried out a bit you're beginning to look quite presentable.'

'Presentable?' Kerry put down her knife and fork, too startled to be anything but honest, as all thoughts of Maybelle evaporated. 'I assume that's not meant as a compliment?'

'Why shouldn't it be?' Declan's eyes were sheer blue-black provocation. 'You were always a cute little brat.'

'And you were always a supercilious jerk,' exclaimed Kerry indignantly. It had never occurred to her before to think much about Declan's opinion of her looks. But now she discovered she didn't like being called merely presentable any more than she liked being called a cute little brat. Even worse, she had a feeling he knew exactly how she felt. It showed in the mocking glitter of his eyes.

'I did my best to keep you in order,' he agreed smugly. 'And you needn't worry. I never take advantage of brats. Not even presentable ones. We both know what that sort of thing can lead to.'

Kerry glared. Did he have to keep harping on the disasters of the past? 'We do, don't we?' she snapped. 'And I'm sure neither of us wants to meet up again in front of an altar.'

'Heaven forbid. My one and only experience in that line was not one I'm anxious to repeat.' Declan spoke without rancor, but his very impassiveness convinced Kerry he meant exactly what he said.

'Was it really so traumatic?' she asked abruptly. 'At the time you didn't seem to mind.'

'Mind what?' He leaned back on his elbows so that his lean body was draped enticingly over the bedspread. Kerry shifted her gaze with an effort.

'You know. Being — well, left in the lurch.' She pushed a hand through her damply tangled hair and stared at a spot of congealed cheese on her plate before blurting, 'It isn't because of me, is it, that you're not married?' She hesitated, as a further disturbing thought came to her. 'That is — you're not, are you? Married, I mean?'

'No,' said Declan. 'I'm not. Are you?'

'You know I'm not. I told you once was enough. I haven't been tempted to try again.'

Nor was she likely to be. Her disastrous marriage had left her with a deep mistrust of relationships that were supposed to be forever, and yet so often turned out to be as temporary as soap.

'Excellent,' said Declan. 'Then we can spend the night together secure in the knowledge that we'll face no interrogation from suspicious spouses in the morning.' He sat up to pour her more wine.

Kerry watched him, knowing that he had no intention of discussing his lack of a spouse, suspicious or otherwise, with her. And she wished he wouldn't talk about their spending the night together in that casual, half-suggestive way. It made her feel as if hot needles were pricking at her skin.

When he handed back the glass, their fingers touched. Kerry glanced up, startled, as electricity quivered up her arm. Declan met her glance. His eyes were inscrutable but she was almost certain he had felt it, too.

She leaned as far away from him as she could and swallowed half the wine in one gulp. Declan's smoky gaze settled on her thoughtfully, but when he said nothing, she became conscious that there was an uneasy intimacy about sitting here with him in this clean but austere hotel room, sipping wine. He should have seemed as comfortably familiar as her cat. But there was nothing comfortable about this new Declan, and the only cat he resembled had to be of the large and predatory variety.

She swallowed the rest of the wine with her eyes closed.

'That's not your favorite Château Green Vengeance,' Declan reproved her, referring to the cheap and sugary rotgut she and her teenage friends had favored whenever they could afford it. 'It's a perfectly good Chianti Classico that deserves to be treated with respect.' He reached over to remove her glass, and his hand brushed up against her leg. At once his eyes narrowed. 'Your jeans are *wet*,' he informed her.

She nodded warily. 'A little. Aren't yours?'

'Not so you'd notice.'

Oh, she'd noticed all right. If his jeans weren't actually wet, they were molded to him just as if they were.

Declan stood up, looked at his watch. 'It's getting late,' he said. 'Time to take them off and get to bed.'

He spoke in his usual clipped, no-nonsense fashion, but she wished he wouldn't look at her with that heavy-lidded, slumbrous gaze that gave a whole new meaning to the term 'bedroom eyes.' And she knew he was doing it on purpose. In his less judgmental moments, Declan had always been something of a tease. But it wasn't fair of him to tease her about bed.

Bed wasn't something she wanted to think about in connection with Declan.

'I haven't any nightclothes,' she said quickly. 'They're in my car. So I'll just have to sleep in my clothes.'

'You'll do nothing of the kind. I'm not into playing nursemaid to foolish young women who catch their deaths sleeping in wet jeans. Take them off at once.'

There was nothing lazy or slumbrous about his gaze now. And he was talking to her just as he had talked to her in the past when she'd wanted to do something that offended his perception of common sense and order.

'I'm not doing any striptease for your benefit,' Kerry retorted, knowing full well that wasn't what he'd meant.

Declan paused in the act of hefting a suitcase on to his bed. 'Oh, aren't you?' he said, turning around. 'That's just as well, isn't it?'

'Why?' asking Kerry, standing up.

'Because I've long since outgrown juvenile diversions of that sort. Now do as you're told and get them off.'

'I will not.'

'All right. You, it seems, have *not* outgrown the need to be dealt with like an underage delinquent.'

Kerry hadn't even got her mouth open to tell him what she thought of his nerve before he was across the room and easing his fingers inside the waistband of her jeans.

'Last chance,' he said, looking her squarely in the eye.

Kerry gulped. He was too close. She couldn't think clearly . . . And then it was too late, because he was already unbuttoning and unzipping and the jeans were down around her knees. Fleetingly, she wished she was wearing lace and satin, instead of her sensible white cotton briefs. Then she pushed the thought away angrily. Cotton was quite good enough for this overbearing, uncivilized bossyboots who seemed to think he had a right to undress her as if she were still a stubborn little girl.

'Sit down,' he said, gesturing at the bed behind her.

Kerry sat, mainly because that way she could seize a corner of the bed-spread and wrap it discreetly around her waist. Although, strangely, she seemed to be feeling more furious than embar-rassed.

'There are laws against sexual harass-ment,' she told him through teeth she was trying not to bare.

Declan gave a bark of a laugh. 'Is that so? But as I don't find shivering young ladies with incipient pneumonia remotely sexual, I doubt if any jury would con-vict. Now then . . . ' He knelt to pull off her socks before yanking the controver-sial jeans over her ankles. 'Right. That's taken care of. What about your sweater?

I suppose you've managed to soak that, as well.'

Kerry glared at the top of his head, longing to curl her fingers in the thick dark hair and give it such a tug that it would come out by the roots. But she didn't do it because she was too busy hanging on to the bedspread. Besides, only children pulled people's hair.

Nice hair, she thought vaguely. Too nice for a man like Declan.

'My sweater is quite dry, thank you,' she told him, in what she hoped was a dignified voice.

Declan reached up, touched the back of his hand to her side. 'Hmm. So it is,' he agreed. 'But hardly comfortable to sleep in. You'd better have one of my shirts.'

'Oh, but I don't want — '

'I don't much care what you want.' He sounded bored and a little impatient but, to Kerry's confusion, instead of resenting his tone, she felt a sudden twinge of sympathy for her old mentor and critic. It couldn't be much fun being obliged to share your hotel room with a damp and irritable young woman who had once deserted you at the altar. In the circumstances, he was being quite reasonable about it. Bossy, but reasonable.

Now if she could only convince him that she was much too big to undress . . .

Or was she? She suppressed the thought before it had a chance to take hold.

Declan rocked back on his heels, and when their eyes met, instead of the exasperated impatience she expected, Kerry saw a flicker of something that might have been surprise. Or — no, maybe it was more like disbelief or — something more immediate that was neither. She heard him swear softly before he stood up rather too quickly and turned to rifle through his suitcase.

'Here,' he said, tossing a white silk shirt over his shoulder. 'Put this on. It should keep you relatively decent.'

'All right,' said Kerry. It seemed

easier and more sensible to give in. 'Don't turn around. You've seen quite enough of me as it is.'

'Hmm. I think I can resist the temptation.' His voice was so brusque and sarcastic that once again Kerry found herself searching for something to throw. But as the only handy objects, apart from the shirt, were two pink socks and a pair of wet jeans, she decided a lofty silence might better make her point.

She stood up, peeled off her pink sweater and bra, and pulled Declan's shirt around her shoulders. It came to about halfway down her thighs, and made her feel slinky and soft and sexy. All the things she particularly didn't want to feel tonight.

Without telling Declan he could turn around, she hurried into the bathroom and shut the door.

Lord, what an abortive holiday this was turning out to be. She stared glumly at her pale face in the mirror. It hadn't improved any since the last time she had looked. And her eyes were still a washed-out mauve instead of their usual soft blue.

Sighing, Kerry turned on the shower and let soap and warm water do their work. She thought about washing her hair, then decided against it because she was damned if she was going to give Declan a chance to make remarks about the folly of going to bed with wet hair — for all she did it all the time when she was home.

It was safe in the shower. Comforting. And after a while it dawned on her that she was deliberately wasting time in order to put off returning to the bedroom and Declan.

'Chicken,' she jeered at herself.

That did it. Throwing her shoulders back, she lifted her chin and marched out of the bathroom feeling as if she were Marie Antoinette going to the tumbril. Except that there was nothing very queenly about tangled blond hair and long bare legs emerging from beneath a man's silk shirt. Nor did

Declan have beheading in mind, as she discovered the moment she stepped through the door.

He was stretched out on the carpet, wearing nothing but a pair of white boxer shorts printed with improbable pink crocodiles. And he was doing push-ups.

Just as he extended his arms to their full, athletic length, Kerry stepped into the room. He looked up, caught an eyeful of shapely leg extending bare and alluring to the edge of the shirt, and collapsed back onto the carpet with a gratifying thud.

Kerry giggled. 'What's this?' she asked. 'Getting in shape for an energetic night of power dreaming? And why *pink* crocodiles?'

Declan did two more slow and suspiciously suggestive push-ups, then rose to his feet. His gaze slid briefly over her scantily clad body. 'Exercise *and* a cold shower, I think,' he remarked, stretching his arms above his head. 'My only hope of getting a night's sleep. And the shorts were a gift from an Australian girlfriend.'

'Oh.' Kerry felt a blush coming on and turned away. She had always been cursed with skin that turned pink at the least provocation. And Declan was one huge provocation. Though why she should blush because a thirty-one-year-old man admitted to having a girlfriend who gave him underwear, she didn't know. She did know she didn't like it. Which was ridiculous. Declan's love life was none of her business.

The blush faded, and she turned back to face him.

He was watching her with a wry little smile pulling at the corner of his mouth. A lock of hair had fallen across his forehead, and a faint sheen of sweat bathed his upper body, causing it to glisten beneath the light. It was a tough, sinuous body. The kind that went with bedrooms, not boardrooms. A body made for action and speed. The kind that Kerry, along with ninety percent of the female population, admired but rarely chose to marry. She swallowed. How was it then, that when she *had* planned to marry Declan, she had desperately tried to ignore the sexuality he seemed to exude as naturally as he — as he took off his clothes? She swallowed again, eyeing the fine dark hair covering his chest with wary appreciation mixed with a healthy dose of trepidation. Too much appreciation could prove dangerous.

When he said, 'Time for that cold shower, I think,' she wondered if he could possibly be thinking the same thing.

His bare arm touched her shoulder as he passed her, and she felt a flicker of irritation as she watched him disappear into the bathroom. How was it that the back view of a man sporting pink crocodiles on his shorts could actually manage to look alluring?

Damn Declan anyway.

Kerry climbed into bed and shut her eyes. They stayed shut as she listened to him singing in the shower in an unexpectedly deep and sexy baritone; as he turned off the water and started to rub himself down; and as he unfastened the bathroom door and walked across the carpet toward the beds.

But when she smelled the faint, leathery scent of soap and water, and felt firm, cool lips touch her cheek, they opened like blue daisies to the sun.

4

'Declan?' Kerry stared at the face hovering just above hers. From this angle it seemed less hawklike, softer somehow. And the blue-black eyes had a hazy, smoky cast. 'Declan, what are you doing?' She took in the brawny arms planted one on either side of her head, and quietly sucked in her breath.

'Kissing you goodnight.' His voice wasn't hazy or smoky. It was clipped and matter-of-fact, the sort of voice she had heard him use a hundred times when he wanted to ease her fears or calm her down.

Kerry released her breath with an unexpected sense of loss and gave up trying to decipher the enigma that was Declan. 'Goodnight then,' she said shortly. 'I hope you sleep well.'

'So do I.' He smoothed a strand of

hair out of her eyes, and straightened.

Kerry lay still, gazing at him in quiet confusion while he looked down at her with his brows drawn together as if he wasn't quite sure what to make of her. Then, after turning off the lamp, he slid between the sheets of the other bed.

Kerry awoke several times during the early part of the night, and each time she heard Declan tossing beneath his covers. Once she even thought she heard him swearing, and wondered if he was having a bad dream. But in the end she fell into a deep, relaxing sleep, and thought no more about the occupant of the other bed until she woke to the sound of the television blaring the morning news, and felt a hand briskly shaking her right shoulder.

'More snow is forecast for the Northern Ontario/Eastern Manitoba region,' announced the electronic voice of the TV. 'Police are advising motorists to stay off the roads . . . The Trans

Canada Highway between Thunder Bay and Kenora is closed due to unsafe driving conditions . . . A number of accidents have been reported . . . Here in Winnipeg . . . '

Kerry shot up in bed, brushing off Declan's hand as her gaze flew toward the screen on which a pink-cheeked young man was standing in front of a familiar office block on Portage Avenue. He was holding a microphone, and white flakes were settling on his hood as he spoke.

'Here in Winnipeg it's snowing,' Kerry finished for him. 'Of course it's snowing. Hardly unusual for March. What's all the fuss?'

'No fuss. Just a weather report. But it's a safe bet your break pads won't be getting through for a day or so.' Declan sounded maddeningly calm.

'Oh.' Kerry put a hand to her mouth, then became conscious that the neck of the shirt she had slept in was drooped revealingly over one shoulder. She moved the hand hastily to her chest. As she had guessed, the top two buttons were undone. She fastened them without looking at Declan, then said brightly, 'So I'll have to find some other way to get home.'

'Such as?'

Kerry removed her gaze from the screen and turned to look at him. He was wearing his jeans and the navy-blue pullover again. And there was a look in his eye that could only be described as incendiary.

'I suppose I could take the bus to Thunder Bay,' she suggested without much enthusiasm.

'It's canceled. Remember?'

So it was. 'Well, then, I guess I'll just have to wait out the storm. Maybe tomorrow — '

'No. Not tomorrow.'

Kerry gaped at him. 'I only came for the weekend. I planned to go to the Easter service today with Lori and leave for home again tomorrow afternoon.'

'Then I'm afraid you're going to have to change your plans.'

Kerry pushed herself up on her elbows. 'What are you talking about? Of course I'm not changing my plans. If I have a choice.'

'You don't have much of a choice.' His lips parted in a small, indecipherable smile.

'Oh? Then perhaps you'd care to explain.' Kerry eyed him with undisguised suspicion. 'It just happens I have work to get back to, so — '

'Work?' he interrupted. 'You have a job?'

'Of course I have a job. How do you think I keep food on my table?'

He shrugged. 'I haven't given it a lot of thought.'

No, he wouldn't have. 'I own a bookshop,' she explained. 'And although my assistant is very capable, she does expect me back. We're having our spring sale next week and she can't handle the business end by herself.'

'And you can?' He sounded surprised and not altogether convinced.

'Of course I can.' Kerry was irked.

101

'I've been running the shop for three years. I bought it with Uncle Charles's legacy.'

'Did you indeed? Well, I'm damned.' Suddenly Declan sank down on the edge of her bed as if he'd been doing it all his life.

Kerry pushed herself back against the pillows, then wished she hadn't because it seemed to amuse him.

'It's all right,' he assured her. 'I never seduce my ex-brides before breakfast.'

'What about after breakfast?' Kerry spoke breathlessly, without thinking. There was something about the scent of him, about this disconcerting intimacy, that undermined her powers of rational thought.

'Ah,' said Declan gravely. 'Let me see now . . . ' He reached for a small black notebook on the stand beside his bed. 'Yes, I believe I could fit you in around — shall we say ten-thirty?'

The eyes that met hers were black and sober, and just for a second, Kerry was taken in. Then she saw his lips twitch briefly, and remembered that this devastating man was Declan, whose code of conduct would never permit him to take advantage of Kerry Fleming.

Her breathing returned to normal. All right. If he wanted to play games . . .

She pretended to consider. 'Hmm. Yes, I . . . No. No, I'm afraid it won't do. Did I tell you I don't do corporate seduction?'

This time it was Declan who drew in his breath. Sharply. 'You little . . . ' He paused as if to gather ammunition. 'Miss Fleming, if I hear one more word from you about the way I make my living, I can promise you'll have more than seduction to think about.' He strummed his fingers on his thigh. 'If you take my meaning. And in case you've forgotten, I don't make idle threats.'

Kerry took his meaning. And she hadn't forgotten he didn't make idle threats. But violence had never been Declan's way, and she didn't believe he'd changed that much in the years since she had left him at the altar.

'You terrify me, Mr. King,' she said lightly.

'Good.' Declan sounded grim.

Kerry edged toward the side of the bed. 'You never were much good at playing the caveman,' she remarked.

'Try me,' he suggested.

Kerry laughed, a light, deliberately taunting laugh, and immediately Declan seized the covers in one hand and flung them down to her ankles. 'OK, time to get up,' he ordered.

Kerry gasped and pulled discreetly on the hem of the shirt he'd lent her.

Declan bent forward, a purposeful glint in his eye.

'All right,' she agreed quickly. There was no point in antagonizing this large and determined man who was currently perched on her bed. 'If you'll just leave me alone to get dressed . . . '

Declan nodded and stood up. 'Hurry up.' He turned away from her and strode toward the door.

Kerry glared, but as he didn't see the glare, it was wasted. 'I don't actually mind how you make your living,' she admitted grudgingly to his back. 'It's just that you keep treating me like — like a stock that hasn't done as well as you expected.'

Declan paused. 'No,' he said evenly. 'You're mistaken. That particular stock has done a lot *better* than I expected.' He disappeared into the hallway before she could form a reply.

Now what did he mean by that? And what had he meant about her having to change her plans? Not that it mattered. Because come snow, ice or high winds she intended to be on her way back to Winnipeg by tomorrow.

' . . . and as reported earlier, police have asked motorists to avoid all but emergency travel — '

Kerry hopped out of bed and bent down to snap off the young announcer's cheerful face. All very well for him. *He* wasn't stranded in Carmody Falls with a sick Saab and a man who actually had the nerve to look sexy in pink crocodile shorts. She closed her eyes, but it didn't help because she could still see Declan on the floor doing push-ups . . .

With a sigh, she turned to pick up her pink sweater and mostly dry jeans, and made her way into the bathroom. Decisions could wait until after breakfast.

When Declan returned, he went immediately to check on her parka. 'Still damp. You'd better have mine,' he said curtly.

'What about you?'

'I have a lighter jacket in my suitcase. It'll do.'

'But — '

'Just do what you're told for once, Kerry.' He sounded more weary now than autocratic. 'It's late. Phil doesn't serve breakfast past ten, and I don't know about you, but I'm hungry.'

And if I don't do as I'm told, you're just bossy enough to make both of us miss breakfast, Kerry guessed. She gave up and allowed him to help her into his parka.

'You look like an animated teepee,' Declan informed her ungallantly.

Kerry didn't reply until they reached the street, at which point she replied that *he* looked like a badly malformed iceberg. She didn't add that it had never occurred to her before that icebergs could look desirable, but with the snow swirling around his black wind-breaker he did look unexpectedly seductive. When he took her arm to hustle her down the street, she jumped.

After that they were too busy fighting their way through the snowdrifts to waste precious breath exchanging unpleasantries.

The TV announcer had exaggerated a bit. In fact the snow was beginning to taper off. All the same, Kerry was glad to reach the steamy warmth of Phil's café and she found she didn't mind the curious stares nearly as much as she had the day before.

They settled for a table near the

counter, and one of Phil's helpers came at once to take their orders for waffles and maple syrup.

As soon as the young woman left, Declan tilted his chair back and pinned Kerry with a look that told her he meant business. 'As soon as we've eaten, I'll talk to Mrs. Kovalik about fixing you up with a room for the next two nights — '

'One night,' said Kerry.

'Two. For one thing, your break pads aren't likely to get through. For another, you're not leaving until Tuesday.'

'Now wait a minute — '

The front legs of Declan's chair snapped down onto the floor. 'The arena is opening tomorrow. I want you to be there — as well as at the dance in the evening.'

'In a pig's ear,' Kerry answered, too stunned to think before she spoke.

Declan shook his head. 'Not good enough.'

'All right, how about, over my dead body?'

'That can be arranged.'

'I suppose it can,' Kerry agreed, 'but there wouldn't be much point. Would there?'

Declan pretended to consider. 'You're right. There wouldn't. Which leaves good, old-fashioned force. As you pointed out, my rusty caveman skills could do with a bit of sharpening up.'

Kerry almost giggled, but managed not to. 'Are you going to throw me over your shoulder and carry me there kicking and screaming?' she asked with interest.

'If I have to.' Declan turned his chair sideways and crossed one leg over the other.

'I see.' Kerry eyed him meditatively. 'Why? You don't need me there. Everyone will gossip about us. And, anyway, I haven't been invited.'

'You have now.'

'That wasn't an invitation. That was an order.'

Declan nodded. 'You catch on fast, don't you, sweetheart?'

Kerry picked up her knife, but discovering there was nothing to slice except Declan, eventually she put it down again. 'You don't have the right to give me orders,' she said finally.

'Oh, yes, I do. You owe me, Kerry Fleming. And this time you're going to pay your debt.'

Kerry stared at him, saw that his eyes were as implacable as the tone of his voice. And it made no sense. Why on earth should Declan want to take her to a dance? Unless . . .

'Declan,' she said. 'Is this your idea of revenge? For my choosing to marry Larry instead of you?'

He swiveled his chair around to face her. ''Revenge is sweet, sweeter than life itself. So say fools.' I'm not a fool, Kerry.'

'Then why — '

'But I do believe in collecting what's owed me.' He swallowed a mouthful of coffee and leaned back.

Kerry sighed, wishing he didn't look so delectable sitting there all casually convinced he had only to raise a finger to have her jumping to carry out his orders. If only . . .

If only what? If only he were old and ugly? But this wasn't about looks or lust. That was what made the whole mess so intolerable. Declan had always come to her aid when she needed him because in the old days he had possessed the strength she lacked. She did owe him. But she *couldn't* do as he insisted. She just couldn't, when every sane instinct she retained urged her to get as far and as fast away from him as she could.

'I'm sorry, but I'm afraid you'll have to do without me,' she said quietly.

'I could, of course. But I've decided not to. I want you with me, Kerry, and this time I'm *not* leaving the decision up to you.'

He meant it. He actually meant it. Kerry tried not to sputter. 'But why?' she groaned. 'Why me? What's wrong with Maybelle?' After she'd spoken, she wondered why the words had almost stuck in her throat.

'Maybelle? Nothing. Except that Phil has been trying to get her to marry him for years.'

'He hasn't!'

'He has, you know. Phil and I are old friends. We had quite a talk yesterday, and he figures she's beginning to come around. He has a successful business, some good investments, and now that he's on the Council with her, Maybelle is beginning to appreciate his worth.'

Kerry shrugged, refusing to admit that Maybelle's matrimonial prospects were of even the smallest interest to her. 'Just the same, if I know Maybelle, she'd choose you as her escort any day.'

'Maybe. But she won't have that option. I'm taking you.'

'Declan,' said Kerry, raising her voice then lowering it hastily when she realized the chatter in the café had suddenly stilled. 'Declan, please understand. I'm not available. You say you don't want revenge — '

'I don't.' Declan tilted his chair back

and gave her what she'd come to think of as his business-shark smile. 'If I'd wanted a suitable revenge, I assure you I'd do better than that. Ask any of my associates.'

Kerry eyed the strong, capable fingers curled around the handle of his cup. Nice fingers. Fingers that . . .

'Declan,' she said, in a voice that came out half strangled. 'You have to believe me. I am *not* staying until Tuesday. The snow will be cleared by tomorrow, and if I have to I can rent a car and pay Lori's brother to drive mine back to Winnipeg when it's ready. He'll be glad to do it.' She paused as the idea sank in. 'Why didn't I think of that before?'

'Because it wouldn't have done you a bit of good if you had. I'd have told the rental company you're a menace on the highways.' Declan smothered a yawn and settled himself back in his chair. 'Which, as I remember, you always were.'

'I was not. I ran Dad's car into a

lamppost once. And got a couple of tickets for speeding — '

'I rest my case,' said Declan.

'That was seven years ago, dammit — '

'Irrelevant. You're not renting any car.'

'Just try and stop me.'

'I don't have to. The rental outfit went out of business three months ago.' He poured a spoonful of sugar carefully into his cup and gave her a smile so bland it made her want to kick him.

When the waffles came, only her protesting stomach stopped Kerry from mashing them in his face.

'I'd rather have chicken pox than go to any dance with you,' she muttered.

Declan's eyes didn't even flicker as he picked up his knife and fork. 'Too bad you don't have a choice then.'

'What's that supposed to mean?'

'You'll see.' He went on eating as if there were no more to be said.

'Declan,' said Kerry, taking a deep, calming breath as she became aware that several heads had turned in their direction. 'I'm truly sorry I caused you so much trouble all those years ago. But I don't owe you the rest of my life.'

'Heaven forbid,' he agreed. 'One weekend should be more than sufficient.'

'No. I'm not doing it.' Kerry went on eating her waffles, irritated with herself as well as with him. She shouldn't have apologized again. Declan only took advantage of apologies.

She refused to look at him after that, but she was conscious of him every second as he sat relaxed in his chair and waited for her to finish. She was also uncomfortably aware of interested looks skimming across to their table and shifting sideways again as soon as she raised her head.

Kerry finished her breakfast without speaking because she knew that if she opened her mouth she was likely to say something that would attract even more attention from Phil's curious patrons. Declan, she suspected, was quietly enjoying her discomfiture.

'Come again,' Phil called after them as they left. 'You two are real good for business.'

'He's got a nerve,' muttered Kerry.

Declan took her arm and said she had only herself to blame if the townsfolk found her presence entertaining.

'If by that you mean I shouldn't have come back to Carmody Falls, you're dead right,' Kerry said viciously.

Declan laughed, which didn't do a thing to improve her temper.

By the time they got back to the Cambrian it had stopped snowing, and the ploughs were busily at work.

'I'll fetch my car. We can drive to church,' said Declan.

'My clothes are still at Dieter's,' Kerry objected. 'He's closed until tomorrow.'

Declan glanced at his watch. 'Mmm. Time's running short. You'll have to go as you are.' He dragged his pullover over his head and tossed it onto a chair.

Mesmerized, Kerry stared at the bare, bronzed expanse of his chest. 'What are you doing?' she gulped.

'Changing.'

When he started to unbuckle his belt, she unfroze and fled into the bathroom.

Dear God. This situation was getting impossible. She couldn't take much more of it. Declan was too — too damn sexy. And she didn't know how to cope with sex in connection with Declan.

Kerry groaned and sank onto the edge of the bath. What was happening to her? It was still only Declan out there. Declan, her old friend and domineering protector. He *couldn't* have changed that much in seven years. She stared glassily at a crack in the mirror above the sink. Did that mean *she* was the one who had changed? Oh, of course she had in a way. She was older and wiser. More practical. But she was still the same person inside. So why did she feel this sense of impending danger?

'Kerry? You can come out now. It's

quite safe.' Declan's voice, amused and mocking, pulled her out of her trance.

She stood up, and after only a brief hesitation edged her way back into the bedroom.

Declan was dressed now, but she didn't feel even remotely safe. He was wearing a sober dark suit, and he looked powerful and dangerous and hypnotic. A banked fire drawing her irresistibly to the promise of conflagration.

She took a step forward and their eyes locked briefly. Then Declan jerked his head at the door behind her. 'Fetch your jacket. It should be dry.' His voice was harsh, breaking the sudden silence that had fallen.

Kerry moistened her lips. 'I can't go to church with you, Declan. I'm not dressed — '

'I'd notice if you weren't.' He was dryly unmoved. 'I said, fetch your jacket.'

'No. Everyone would stare. I look like Cinderella and you're dressed like . . . '

Like the Prince of Darkness. 'Like the Chairman of the Board,' she finished lamely. 'I can't possibly go with you, Declan.'

'So you said.' He flicked a brief glance over her jeans and pink sweater, then without another word picked up his coat and left the room.

Kerry stood with her mouth gaping open as the door snapped shut behind him.

He was leaving. Without her. Just like that. And he hadn't even bothered to argue.

Stunned, she walked across to the door and leaned against it before trailing dazedly over to her bed. For a few seconds she stared blankly at the sensible beige bedspread. Then she sat down with a faint creak of springs.

Declan had gone without her. He had taken her at her word — which, deep down, she had never expected him to do. And she felt an emptiness, as if she had lost something vital and warm and exciting that she hadn't even known she

wanted until she didn't have it anymore.

He'd be back of course. After church.
Even so, she felt abandoned. The man
she had trusted to look after her
through thick and thin and snowstorms
had left her to her own devices as if it
were no concern of his whether she
went with him or not.

Probably because it *wasn't* a concern.
The thought was an unpleasant shock.

She stared through the window at the
plough piling snow along the edge of
the sidewalk. Did she actually *want*
Declan back in her life then? In a way, a
startlingly physical way, perhaps she
did. But she certainly didn't want his
bossiness, his unfair conviction that she
was a hopeless twenty-five-year-old
delinquent. They had done nothing but
strike sparks off each other from the
moment they'd met up in Phil's café.
Maybe it was just as well he'd gone to
church without her. She didn't need his
company. Hadn't needed it for years.
Any more than he'd ever needed hers.

Kerry stood up and moved into the bathroom to check her parka. It was dry. That was something. She had just pulled it on, thinking she might as well walk off her sudden restlessness, when she heard the sound of a key in the lock.

She stared at the door, heart pounding.

It opened with unexpected force as Declan strode across the threshold looking businesslike. His gaze swept the room and finally came to rest on her pink socks. 'Where are your boots?' he demanded.

'In the cupboard, of course, but — '

He didn't wait for her to finish, but marched across to the cupboard, flung it open and scooped up her elegant black boots.

'Put them on,' he said, holding them out.

'Declan, I said I wasn't going . . . '

'Last chance,' he said imperturbably.

They were the same words he had spoken last night. And there was a light in his eye that made Kerry think he was in a mood to relish battle.

'Listen,' she said. 'You can't — '

'Oh, yes, I can.'

Before she had a chance to guess what was coming, Declan had acted. One muscular arm went under her hips and jerked her feet off the floor. The other, still holding the boots, pulled the door closed behind them. Kerry found herself being carried down the stairs at a run. Her head was hanging over his shoulder, and when they reached the lobby she lifted it in time to encounter the startled gaze of Mrs. Kovalik.

'Say one word, and I'll tell her this is the way you get your kicks,' growled Declan out of the side of his mouth. 'You'll keep Carmody Falls in gossip right through Christmas.'

For a moment Kerry was too stunned by his audacity to answer. Declan, apparently taking her silence for acquiescence, announced cheerfully to Mrs. Kovalik that Miss Fleming had unfortunately managed to get her boots wet.

'That's what I like to see,' said Mrs. Kovalik. 'Gentlemen *behaving* like gentlemen.'

By the time Kerry had stopped choking and got her breath back, she was installed on the passenger seat of Declan's steel-gray, rented Lincoln and he was briskly tucking a rug around her knees.

5

Declan finished arranging the rug around his squirming cargo, snapped in her seatbelt, and moved to the other side of the car.

'Comfortable?' he asked.

Kerry's hands inched toward the door.

'Forget it,' said Declan. 'My caveman skills aren't as rusty as I thought. As you may have noticed.'

'I've noticed,' replied Kerry. 'And I'm not impressed.'

'Oh?' He paused with the key in the ignition. 'You want me to impress you?'

'No,' said Kerry. 'I want you to let me out of this car.'

Declan laid his arm along the back of the seat. 'No you don't. You're putting up a fight out of habit and sheer bloody-mindedness. Aren't you?'

Kerry wriggled indignantly.

'Very nice,' said Declan. 'You've cultivated quite a sexy wriggle since last we met.' He leaned over to trail his fingers through her hair.

Kerry jerked her head away at once.

'Stop it,' she said, stifling a quick, unwanted flush of pleasure. 'And for your information, I'm putting up a fight because I refuse to attend the service with . . . ' She stopped. Declan was stroking his thumb slowly down her neck. 'With you,' she finished, catching her breath.

'Really?' He spread his fingers, slid them inside her parka.

'Declan . . . ' Her voice was a moan of desperation. 'Declan, please . . . '

He withdrew his hand at once. 'Very well. Out you get.'

'But — '

'Or would you prefer to climb down off your high horse and come with me?'

'My purse,' she muttered. 'I left it — '

'In the trunk,' he said tersely. 'I took the precaution of putting it there while you were being maidenly in the bathroom.'

Kerry glared. 'You think of everything, don't you?'

'I try to.'

'All right, tell me why my going to church with you matters.'

'Let's say it pleases me to return with my ex-bride to the scene of my notorious rejection.'

In other words, he wanted to humiliate her. Which was fair enough, she supposed. Except that it wasn't like Declan to be vindictive.

'I thought you said you didn't mind being rejected.' She stared fixedly at a dog pushing its nose through the snow.

'I said I wasn't heartbroken. However, it wasn't one of my more ego-boosting experiences. What it did teach me is that the best way to avoid looking like a fool is to confront the whispers and the gossip head-on.'

Oh. So that was why he was being so hard and overbearing. He was determined to make her confront *her* embarrassment head-on.

And he was right. Damn him.

'All right. You win,' she snapped.

Declan nodded noncommittally and turned the key in the ignition.

Why was it that he always got his way? Kerry wondered, as the car rumbled to life and drew smoothly away from the curb. And why had she given in to him as usual? It seemed the more she saw of Declan the more it appeared that nothing had changed in seven years. Yet what did she really know about the man her old idol had become? He had acquired a reputation for ruthlessness in business. And long ago she had given him reason to deal ruthlessly with her . . .

She glanced doubtfully at his profile. He didn't look ruthless. He looked confident, purposeful — and unfairly handsome. She frowned, adjusting the hood of her parka as she realized they were already pulling up outside the church.

Kerry swallowed. The last time she

had been with Declan in this church, she had ended up marrying Larry. Who had deserted her. Unexpectedly, her lip began to quiver. So she bit it.

'Watch it,' snapped Declan, observing the lip as he helped her out of the car. 'Don't let them think you're ashamed. For all you probably should be.'

Kerry stopped wanting to cry. 'I'm not ashamed,' she whispered indignantly. 'I'm just — remembering.'

His eyes were hooded as he took her arm. 'So am I,' he said in a clipped voice. 'Now hold your head up and smile.'

As he began to march her toward the small knot of people who had suddenly found a reason to hover in the entranceway instead of going straight into church, Kerry found herself doing exactly as Declan said. All at once it was a matter of pride to hold her head up and smile.

To her amazement, when she came up to them, most of the people smiled back.

'Nice to see you again, Kerry,' said Mrs. Maki, who had been running the town's library ever since Kerry could remember.

'Welcome back,' said Rosie Ash, who worked at the general store.

'Thank you. It's nice to be back,' Kerry said. And it was. Declan had been right all along. Perhaps if she had smiled more enthusiastically at the elders in Phil's café, they, too, would have welcomed her back. She turned to tell Declan so.

And the smile froze on her face.

A bright red sports car had just pulled into the church parking lot, and out of it stepped a pair of bright red boots followed by a bright red coat and a lot of curly blond hair beneath a jaunty red hat.

'Declan!' squealed the woman Kerry automatically christened the Red Scream. 'You've come.' She ran through the snow with her arms outstretched and her baby-blond curls bouncing on her neck. Ignoring Kerry, she flung her arms around Declan.

'Maybelle,' said Declan, not batting an eyelid as he smilingly removed the clutching arms and restored them to their owner's sides. 'How are you?'

'Oh, a whole lot better for seeing you,' the woman gushed.

'Hi, Maybelle,' said Kerry.

Maybelle stepped back, her big, blue eyes opening very wide. 'Kerry Simms,' she exclaimed, with emphasis on the Simms. 'No one told me *you* were in town.' She glanced appraisingly at Kerry's neat but unfestive figure in parka and jeans. 'Oh, dear. *Don't* tell me you've fallen on hard times.'

'I won't,' Kerry assured her. 'As it happens — '

Declan's hand tightened around her elbow. 'That'll do,' he said softly. 'Shall we go in?' It wasn't a question, Kerry knew.

'Yes,' she said. 'Let's.' She didn't add, *Before I shove a handful of snow down someone's neck.* But she thought it. And Declan knew it. She could tell from the repressive line of his mouth.

All the same, she let him lead the two of them into church. It was preferable to watching Maybelle try to wrap herself around Declan while clinging ostentatiously to his arm.

'You'll be sitting at the front, won't you, Declan?' Maybelle whispered, favoring him with her candy-coated smile.

'Of course,' he replied, giving Kerry a look that dared her to argue.

Before she found a way to object, he was marching her down the aisle in full view of the gaping congregation. When she tried to pull back, he maintained his grip on her arm and made her take her place beside him in the very front pew. Without being asked, Maybelle followed.

Kerry glared at Declan. Of course he had deliberately chosen this opportunity to face down the stares and whispers their presence together was certain to provoke. But that didn't make his high-handedness any easier to take.

When he returned her look with a cool smile and laid a hand lightly on her knee, she hit it off as if it were a fly.

'Don't make a scene,' said Declan out of the side of his mouth. 'We're here to prove you've finally learned to behave.'

Kerry gripped her hands in her lap, stared straight ahead and pretended to ignore him. It was the only way she could prevent herself from giving him her uncensored opinion of overbearing toads who thought they had a right to give her orders — which would most certainly have caused the scene they both wanted to avoid.

Sitting quietly in the dim mauve light, Kerry didn't hear much of the service. Once her anger at Declan began to cool, she found herself overwhelmed by memories of the past. Of standing beside Declan in her turquoise wedding gown dreaming, in fear and excitement, of the night that lay ahead. Of Larry exploding into the church to shatter the dream. Or had it been a nightmare? She felt the hard pressure of Declan's arm against her side, and after a while it came to her that the emotions of that momentous day were no longer as clear as they had been. All she knew at this moment was that she was conscious of Declan, and of no one else. Of Declan who had kidnapped her, brought her here by force — and then made her face down her fears.

With a start, Kerry realized the Reverend Jonathan was announcing the last hymn. She raised her head and began to sing with an enthusiasm born of guilt for her lack of attention, and a determination to show Declan she wasn't intimidated.

Five minutes later, with Declan and Maybelle beside her, she joined the rest of the congregation in the bright, cold air of early spring.

The sun was shining through a break in the clouds, and suddenly it really seemed like Easter.

There was no escaping the towns-people now. The three of them were immediately surrounded by familiar faces. Kerry waited for the inevitable nosy questions, for the whispers, and the veiled glances and the snickers. But there were no questions, only friendly greetings. And if there were whispers she didn't hear them.

When she looked up at Declan she knew why.

Anyone observing that tough, dominant stance and the formidable line of his jaw would know without being told that any impudent question would be met with the cutting response it deserved. Yet his natural charisma was as much in evidence as always, and Kerry thought she understood now why the Town Council had been so anxious for his participation in an event that, for Carmody Falls, would likely be the highlight of the year.

'Declan,' cooed Maybelle, as the small crowd at last began to drift away, 'I do hope I can persuade you to come to lunch.'

'Thank you,' said Declan. 'That's

kind of you. Unfortunately Kerry and I have already made plans.'

They had? It was the first Kerry had heard of it.

'Oh, what a shame.' Maybelle pouted prettily. 'And I suppose the O'Malleys have asked you for dinner . . . ?'

'Yes.' Declan's smile was politely regretful. 'But if it's company you want, I believe Phil — '

'Oh, Phil . . . ' Maybelle fluttered her hands.

'We'll look forward to seeing you tomorrow then,' said Declan firmly, and led Kerry back to the Lincoln.

'She's furious,' said Kerry, discovering she wasn't angry with Declan after all. 'Why *didn't* you accept her invitation?'

He opened the car door. 'Because, as I told her, you and I have plans. In you get.'

'What, and miss the chance to be manhandled again?' she asked flippantly.

Declan paused with his fingers on the

handle. His eyes took on a dangerous glitter. 'You don't know when to quit, do you, Kerry? You never did. All right. I aim to please.'

Kerry opened her mouth, but Declan's hands were already on her waist, and the next moment she found herself being dumped forcibly onto the seat. Declan slammed the door.

'Ouch. I'll have bruises on my backside,' Kerry grumbled, as he swung himself in behind the wheel.

'You deserve them.' Declan was unsympathetic. 'Grow up, Kerry.'

Kerry gritted her teeth. 'If I'm such a child,' she said irritably, 'I can't see why you want me with you at Carmody Falls' Event of the Year.'

Declan switched on the engine. 'Why not? You'll be convincing enough in the role I want you to play. You won't mistake my intentions. And you're available.' He slanted her a glance that failed to unclench her teeth, and shifted the Lincoln into gear.

'I am *not* available,' Kerry said.

'Can't you get it into your thick head that I have to get back to work?'

'You'll get back,' said Declan. '*After the Opening.*'

Kerry was too irritated to answer. Besides, there was no point. She knew of old that when Declan was in his brick-wall mood it was absolutely futile to argue. Which didn't mean she meant to let him have his way. Not this time.

Lifting her chin, she gazed distantly at the gray piles of snow beside the road and maintained a frosty silence until they reached the hotel.

Declan went straight up to the counter and asked Mrs. Kovalik if she had a room for Mrs. Simms for the night.

'Oh, dear me. I'm afraid not.' Mrs. Kovalik ran a harried eye over her reservations book. 'We're booked right up because of tomorrow's celebrations. You could try Oscar's Cabins.'

Declan shook his head. 'No. Mrs. Simms needs someone to keep an eye on her.' He frowned. 'She'd better stay with me again.'

'Well, I suppose if it's only for one night . . . ' Mrs. Kovalik looked doubtful. Kerry saw that the rumors had already started, and opened her mouth to say that she most definitely did *not* need looking after.

'Maybe two nights,' said Declan, forestalling her. 'At the most.' He turned to Kerry. 'Coming, Sis?'

Kerry considered the alternative, which was probably to be manhandled again, and made her way up the stairs with what she hoped was dignified poise. But as soon as they were back in Declan's room she turned on him and snapped, 'It's obvious you don't want me cluttering up your room. Oscar's Cabins will suit me just fine.'

He raised an eyebrow. 'Will they? You like bugs? Oscar's has a fine selection, so I'm told.'

'Oh.' Slowly Kerry unzipped her parka and took it off.

Declan gave her a maddening little

smile and lowered himself into a chair.

Lord, why did he have to look so — so powerfully seductive in that suit? Kerry swallowed as he loosened his tie.

'Declan, we can't stay cooped up here together all day,' she said desperately.

'And all night.' He removed the tie.

Kerry seized the back of the other chair and held on to it as if her life depended on it. 'Declan, this is ridiculous. We have to do something — '

'Do we? Well, I don't know about you, but I propose to get changed — '

'I can't get changed. I don't have any clothes.'

'That sounds promising. But sadly inaccurate.' Declan eyed her sweater and jeans with disfavor.

'Stop it,' said Kerry, wishing she could stamp her foot at him as she had done when she was younger. 'You know perfectly well what I mean.'

Declan leaned his head against the back of his chair. 'Mmm. I'm afraid I do. All right. After lunch we'll track down Dieter and retrieve your luggage. Following which I propose to spend the afternoon getting on with the work I brought with me. You, sweetheart, may amuse yourself — quietly, I hope — with one of those unseemly books I have no doubt you packed in your suitcase.'

'Unseemly,' scoffed Kerry, more rattled by Declan's mockery than she wanted to admit. 'Declan, how stuffy can you get?'

'Extremely,' said Declan. 'When necessary. As it frequently seems to be in your case.'

Kerry shook her head. 'That may have been true seven years ago. It isn't anymore. People change, you know.'

'Do they? I haven't seen much evidence of it so far.'

She knew, somehow, that he wasn't teasing now. He meant it. 'That's because you haven't tried to see,' she said, hurt, and yet not understanding why it mattered. She moved away from the chair without thinking, and stood gazing down at him with her hands curled tightly at her sides.

For a moment their looks held.

'Haven't I, sweetheart?' he reached for her wrist and pulled her up against his knees.

She trembled, although the room wasn't cold. 'You know you haven't.'

'Then why don't you show me how you've changed?'

His voice was unusually soft, and Kerry pulled away from him at once, not trusting the blue-black glitter in his eyes. And yet — this was Declan. He couldn't be asking what she thought he was asking. Could he?

'What do you mean?' she whispered, collapsing into the other chair and wrapping her arms around her chest as she always did when she felt vulnerable.

His crooked smile hatched a nest of butterflies in her stomach. 'What would you like me to mean?'

'I — I don't . . . don't know. I don't want you to mean anything.' She took a deep breath. 'I just want you to accept that I'm not a child.'

'Mmm.' He smoothed a hand over his jaw. 'I suppose I have to concede that. Reluctantly.'

'You'd like it if I were still a little girl, wouldn't you?' she accused, resenting his detachment, resenting everything about him in this moment. 'Less trouble for you, of course, because that way you'd always have the upper hand.' She lowered her eyes. 'Unfortunately it isn't that simple.'

Nothing was simple anymore. Because somehow Declan, the severe, honorable guardian she had once loved and hated in the same breath, had become something else entirely. Something that frightened her and made her want to run from him at the same time as it dragged her helplessly into his orbit.

It was all so desperately confusing . . .

'I believe I already have the upper hand,' said Declan rising abruptly. 'And I haven't the slightest interest in keeping you in short dresses and ribbons. Let's go to lunch.'

'Lunch?' echoed Kerry.

'Yes. A light one, I think. We'll be dining with the O'Malleys tonight.'

'I won't,' said Kerry. 'I haven't been invited.'

'You,' Declan explained as he shrugged off his jacket, 'have just become 'and escort.' I was asked to bring a guest.'

'They probably expect you to bring Maybelle.'

'No, they don't. I told them I was bringing you.'

'But why? There's no need . . . '

'Because you owe me. That's why.'

He was being a brick wall again. Kerry went to pick up her parka. When she turned around, Declan was unbuckling his belt.

'Going to hide in the bathroom again?' he taunted.

'Yes,' hissed Kerry through her teeth. Was he doing it deliberately? Making her stomach churn and her legs go woolly at the knees. No, surely he couldn't be? To him she would always be silly little Kerry Fleming who fell for boys like Oliver and Larry. It would never occur to him that she might find him attractive. It hadn't seriously occurred to her until yesterday.

She spun into the bathroom with a toss of her head. Behind her she heard Declan's smug chuckle.

When she peered cautiously around the door ten minutes later, he was once again dressed in sweater and jeans.

To Kerry's relief, they managed to get through lunch with relatively little friction. This was mainly because she had come to the reluctant conclusion that it would be much easier to survive this day — and the night to follow — by falling in with Declan's plans. She wasn't fond of the bugs that apparently went with the decor at Oscar's, and until either the bus started running again or her break pads showed up, she had no choice but to get along with Declan as best she could.

'Did you see Maybelle in church?'

Phil asked them just as they were leaving. The big man had the look of an anxious puppy.

Declan nodded. 'Yes. I told her you were free this evening.'

Phil's brow smoothed out. 'You did? I thought perhaps she meant to ask you — '

'Maybelle and I are friends,' said Declan. 'Nothing more.'

'Maybelle wants to be a lot more than friends,' Kerry muttered, the moment the two of them were outside.

'Does she? You have some objection to that? Apart from Phil's interest, of course.'

'No. I haven't. Why should I?' She kicked a lump of ice across the sidewalk.

'That's what I was wondering.'

Kerry pressed her lips together and said nothing as they made their way back to the Cambrian. She didn't know what to say. Declan had hit a raw nerve, because her hackles had risen the moment she'd taken in that Maybelle was still pursuing Declan. And she had no right or reason to care. No reason at all. *Didn't* care, dammit . . .

As soon as they got back to the hotel, Declan headed for his car.

'Where are you going?' Kerry demanded with sudden suspicion.

He smiled, almost as if he'd guessed she was thinking about Maybelle. 'We are going to Dieter's to fetch your luggage. As I remember, he only lives a few blocks from his garage.'

Yes, of course he did. Why hadn't she thought of that?

'All right.' She swallowed, and then added a belated, 'Thank you.'

'My pleasure,' said Declan, looking anything but pleased.

Dieter, wearing earmuffs that made him look like a kindly potato, greeted them on the steps with the news that Kerry's break pads wouldn't be installed until Wednesday. At the earliest. But he handed Declan the keys to his garage when the problem of Kerry's luggage was explained.

He would, Kerry thought morosely. No one in Carmody Falls had ever trusted *her* with their keys.

Soon her bags had been loaded into the trunk of the Lincoln and the garage keys returned to their owner.

'Thanks,' said Kerry, as Declan handed her back into the car. 'Lucky I only brought two suitcases. It would have been hard to handle any more on the bus.'

'Would it? But you won't be taking the bus.'

'Of course I will,' said Kerry. 'Tomorrow.' She added that in case he still harbored notions she was staying.

Declan waited until they were on their way before replying. 'Didn't I make myself clear? You're not taking any bus tomorrow.'

'Oh?' said Kerry sweetly. 'Then how am I supposed to get to Thunder Bay? Last time I looked, Carmody Falls had no airport. And I seem to have mislaid my magic carpet.'

'I recommend a broomstick,' Declan

drawled. 'Preferably applied to your backside.'

'Oh, do you?' Kerry stroked her knuckles in her lap. 'Declan, this caveman business seems to have gone to your head. That kind of uncivilized suggestion went out of fashion along with lace caps and chastity belts.'

'Did it? But then I've never been much interested in fashion. And uncivilized sounds very appealing at the moment.' He flicked her a cool glance that would have made her hit him if they hadn't been driving on an exceptionally slippery patch of road.

As it was, she contented herself with saying, 'Maybe so, but the courts are very interested in intimidation.'

Declan snorted. There was no other way to describe the sound that came from his throat. 'And what court in its right mind would ever believe you could be intimidated?' he asked. 'I've been trying to keep you in order for half a lifetime. So far with very limited success.'

Kerry eyed him doubtfully. Was he serious? No, not entirely. There was an annoying little grin tugging at the edge of his mouth.

She was still forming a reply when he went on, 'There's really no need to look at me as if you'd like to disembowel me. I'm driving to Thunder Bay myself on Tuesday.'

'Are you? So what you're suggesting is — '

'I'm suggesting you come with me. It's not a long drive. Fortunately.'

'Oh.' Kerry frowned, digesting Declan's offer. It was obvious he wasn't exactly panting for her company on the drive. But for some reason of his own he was determined to keep her with him until Tuesday. And having him as her chauffeur would certainly make things easier in one way. Except that she had planned to be home by Tuesday, and she wasn't at all sure she wanted to put herself under any further obligation to a man who was able to get under her skin by the simple act of opening his mouth.

His annoyingly attractive mouth. Declan was bad enough when he was being bossy and chauvinistic — she was used to that — but he was worse when he chose to be helpful. She had no defences against his generosity.

'I couldn't think of asking you to drive me,' she said finally.

'Then don't. Just accept that I'm going to, and be grateful.'

Did he *have* to keep harping on gratitude? She did owe him something, but if he thought gratitude meant a lot of groveling and saluting, he was out of luck.

'Thank you,' she said, in her most condescending voice. 'I'll certainly consider your offer.'

When she stole another glance at him, she suspected she'd overdone the condescension. He looked as though he was trying not to laugh.

Kerry scowled, and maintained a cool silence until they were once more in the Cambrian's lobby. Mrs. Kovalik came bustling from the back.

'Good news,' she called. 'One of my guests has canceled. I can give you a room of your own now, Mrs. Simms.'

'Thank heaven for small mercies,' muttered Declan.

'I'll second that,' said Kerry.

He turned his head, ran a contemplative eye over the pugnacious set of her jaw, and flashed her his crooked white smile. It was a smile that made her stomach curdle and turned her legs limp as spaghetti. And suddenly it wasn't relief she felt at all. It was something that was horribly like disappointment, washing over her in great foaming waves.

In that moment Kerry knew with deadly certainty that she would have to move far and fast if she wanted to prevent the man who had once been her beloved protector from becoming lethally dangerous to her health.

6

Kerry's solitary bedroom was very much like the one she'd shared with Declan, except that Mrs. Kovalik had added a welcome touch of warmth by placing a bowl of Easter lilies in the window. Even so, Kerry felt cold, and after unpacking and hanging up her clothes, she slumped down in a chair that was identical to the ones in Declan's room, and hugged her arms to her chest. A moment later she jumped up again and began to pace back and forth across the room.

When she collided with the edge of the dresser she stopped to put a hand to her head. It felt light, as though it didn't belong to her. So did her body. Dear heaven, what was happening to her? She had always known Declan had the power to affect her emotions. But this feeling that had slammed into her down there in the lobby and was causing her to walk into furniture was something different — an explicitly physical sensation that stirred her as she'd never been stirred before.

In the past she had loved Declan, resented him, been warily grateful. In that order. So how could it be that now, after all this time, she appeared to be suffering from a serious case of lust?

Kerry closed her eyes, passed a hand over her forehead, and sank onto the edge of the nearest bed.

'Don't be a fool, Kerry Fleming,' she said out loud.

Was she a total fool? She glared at a picture of pink herons contemplating a sunset. Declan *had* given certain signals that he wasn't entirely oblivious to her charms. But they had been light-hearted, mocking signals dispatched to pretty, flighty, little Kerry.

That wasn't, and could never be, enough. After the fiasco of her marriage, if there was ever another man in her life he would be for always. Declan wouldn't be.

She had made that decision long ago, and nothing had happened since to change her mind. Of course it hadn't.

Swallowing a sigh, Kerry tossed back her hair, stiffened her spine and picked up the phone to arrange her Saab's journey home.

*   *   *

'Good evening, Kerry. It is Kerry, isn't it?' Bespectacled Mr. O'Malley, the Mayor of Carmody Falls, beamed at her from the doorstep of his stately white house on the hill.

'Kerry! My dear, how nice to see you.' Mrs. O'Malley, the mayor's stout wife, greeted her with delighted effusion. Too delighted, Kerry decided. Mrs. O'Malley would have preferred to welcome Maybelle.

Well, she wasn't Maybelle, the Lady in Red. She was Kerry Fleming in a plain but figure-hugging black dress.

And she was going to carry off this one evening as Declan's partner with poise, dignity and restraint. Perhaps, sometime in the future, he would think back and remember that she hadn't let him down.

There would be no evenings after this one.

Everything went according to plan at first. Kerry listened with interest to Mr. O'Malley's stories about the history of the town, and Declan admired Mrs. O'Malley's collection of china dolls. Then dinner was served in a paneled dining room furnished in antique mahogany.

It wasn't until desert was served that disaster struck.

All would have been well if Declan hadn't chosen to shift his position slightly at the precise moment when the young woman who had been hired to cater the meal was placing blueberry cheesecake in front of Kerry, whose eyes were immediately drawn to the riveting play of muscles across his shoulders. She was just thinking how glamorous he looked in his pressed and expensive dark suit, when she discovered the blueberry cheesecake was no longer on a plate.

A sticky blue stain oozed across Mrs. O'Malley's pale green linen placemat.

'Oh, I am so sorry,' Kerry gasped, scooping blueberries frantically back onto her plate. 'I can't think how it happened . . . '

'Never mind,' said Mrs. O'Malley in a strangled voice. 'I expect it will wash out.'

Mr. O'Malley leaned over to pat Kerry's hand. 'Of course it will wash out. Think nothing of it, my dear.'

'Still playing with your food, Kerry?' murmured Declan. 'Aren't you getting a little old for that?'

The remark was intended for her ears alone, but Kerry felt her temper flare at once. Smug, odious, unfairly attractive man. If he thought he was getting away with that, he was wrong.

But she mustn't cause a scene . . .

Her lips parted in her best angelic smile.

She waited until Declan had picked up his fork, then eased off her black patent shoe. As he took his first mouthful of cheesecake, she extended her right leg discreetly, touched her big toe to his ankle, and began to work her way deliberately up his calf.

The only sign Declan gave that he was aware of her activities beneath the table came from the slight twitching of a muscle in his jaw. He ignored her for a while, then calmly laid down his fork and caught her wandering toes in his hand.

Kerry gasped as, without changing his expression, he began to move his thumb in slow, tormenting circles back and forth across the ball of her foot. She tried to pull away, but strong fingers closed around her instep, allowing him to continue his excruciating massage.

At last, when she could bear it no longer, Kerry started to giggle. Uncontrollably.

Declan released her at once, and she thrust her foot back into its shoe.

'My dear?' Mr. O'Malley peered at her over his spectacles. 'Is something wrong?'

Mrs. O'Malley narrowed her eyes and said nothing.

'No,' Kerry choked. 'No, I'm sorry. I — um — '

'Kerry has very sensitive skin,' said Declan blandly. 'I expect something tickled her funny bone.'

Mrs. O'Malley glanced at him sharply, but Mr. O'Malley nodded and said he quite understood.

Kerry finished her cheesecake in a choked silence while the conversation buzzed around her. She didn't dare look at Declan.

To her enormous relief, the rest of the visit passed without incident, and when it came time to leave, she was able to keep her smile politely in place as she thanked the O'Malleys for an exceptionally delightful evening.

'You — you toad,' she sputtered

furiously the moment they were safely in the Lincoln.

'Don't call me names,' said Declan, shifting gears.

'Why not? You'd no right to make a fool of me in front of our hosts.'

'I didn't. You did that to yourself.'

'Because of the cheesecake? Haven't you ever spilled anything?' she demanded.

'Not because I was eyeballing the talent,' replied Declan dryly.

Kerry winced. So he'd noticed. 'I wasn't — '

'Yes, you were. Very flattering. I enjoyed it. In fact if I hadn't felt I'm a little old to be caught playing footsie under the table, I might have enjoyed that, too.'

Did he mean it? It was impossible to tell, because he was looking straight ahead as if his thoughts were entirely on the road. In any case her attempt to put him in his place had surely backfired. What on earth must the O'Malleys have thought? She glanced at Declan again. Was she imagining the faint quiver at the corner of his mouth?

'Declan, are you laughing at me?' she asked indignantly.

'I'm trying very hard not to,' he admitted. 'Having had first-hand experience of your retaliatory instincts, I'm not inclined to incite them while I'm driving.'

'Toad,' said Kerry. But she didn't really mean it this time, because all at once her heart felt much lighter. Declan wasn't angry. She hadn't let him down after all.

Ten minutes later, when she turned to bid him goodnight outside her door, she heard herself murmuring instead, 'I suppose you wouldn't like to come in?'

'What a charming invitation,' he replied in a tone that sent shivers up her spine. 'Thank you. I will. If you'll excuse me for a moment . . . ?'

Kerry gulped. 'I wasn't suggesting — '

'I should hope not,' he said solemnly.

'I just thought we could talk,' she explained, edging her way through the door. 'Like we used to. When I was a kid.'

'Mmm. But you're not a kid any longer. Are you, Ms. Fleming?' He touched two fingers lightly to her waist. 'Did you wear this slinky black dress just to prove it?'

Once again Kerry had to force herself to smile. She had worn the dress because she knew it flattered her slim figure, but also because she had thought if sufficiently colorless to correspond with Declan's sober tastes. And now he was making it sound as though she had put it on to make herself appear more seductive and sophisticated than she was.

'What did you expect?' she asked. 'Pink taffeta with puffed sleeves and frills?'

'Very suitable,' said Declan.

There was no reason why that should hurt. Of course there wasn't. Kerry tried to maintain her smile, realized it was turning into a grimace and turned away.

Declan stopped her by putting his knuckles under her chin and making her face him. 'OK, so I was being unfair,' he said softly. 'Don't sulk, Kerry. It makes you look like a kitten fluffing up its fur to scare a tiger.'

Kerry shrugged away from him. 'And you're the tiger, I suppose. A lordly, prowling sort of animal who keeps his women in their place.'

'Why, thank you,' said Declan gravely. 'I do my best.'

'How fortunate that I'm not one of your women then,' she scoffed.

'Fortunate for you? Probably.' He propped himself against the doorframe, thick lashes hiding his eyes. 'Undoubtedly fortunate for me.'

Briefly, Kerry considered throwing a few pillows. Followed by a lamp and the odd bar of soap. But she caught the quick flash of a malevolent smile, and suspected he was inciting her to do exactly that.

Why? To convince himself she really was the child he thought her? Or so he'd have an excuse to retaliate. With Declan it was impossible to tell. It always had been.

When she didn't respond to his gibe, he touched her briefly on the cheek and said he'd be back in a few minutes. Before Kerry could collect her wits to tell him she'd changed her mind and he needn't bother, he had disappeared into the room next to hers.

She closed her door and went to stare out of the window at the flickering lights reflected on the snow. What in the world had she let herself in for? Of course Declan wouldn't harm her in any way, but the less time she spent with him the better. Every sane instinct she'd ever had convinced her of that. The trouble was, sanity didn't seem to have much chance when it came to her feelings about Declan.

By the time he knocked on her door ten minutes later, Kerry had changed out of the black dress and into a blue velour robe — then into the dress again, and back into the robe three more times. She was about to put on the dress for the fourth time when she heard his knock. 'Hell,' she muttered, hurrying to open the door, and well aware that she probably looked rattled, disheveled and overly pink in the face. She was still refastening the belt of her blue robe.

Declan hadn't changed out of his suit. His eyebrows rose when he took in her appearance. 'No need to undress on my account,' he murmured. 'It's been a long day.'

Kerry was furious to feel her face turning pinker. She hadn't yet adjusted to this new Declan who made teasingly suggestive remarks, then turned right around and treated her like the delinquent he seemed to think she was.

She waved regally at the nearest chair. 'I wasn't planning to take anything off. Won't you have a seat?'

Declan ignored the chair and went to sit on the bed.

Kerry wasn't comfortable with him there. He had been distracting enough last night. This evening she found him even more disturbing. Just looking at him seemed to give her goose bumps, and the sight of him on her bed made her want to go over to him and . . . No. Most definitely no.

'Wouldn't you prefer a chair?' she asked in a high, unnatural voice that in her ears sounded shrewish instead of gracious as she'd intended.

'No, thanks.' He brushed an imaginary speck off his sleeve.

'You'd be more comfortable . . . '

'I'm fine, thank you.' He loosened his tie and leaned back on his elbows.

Kerry wasn't fine. She was irritated, uncomfortable and on edge. And her heart was beating much too fast. But Declan looked about as moveable as a mountain. Did he have any idea of the effect he was having on her blood pressure?

'All right. If you're sure,' she said abruptly. 'I guess we'd better get on with it. It's getting late.'

'I beg your pardon?'

Oh, Lord, there were those eyebrows again. 'I meant, get on with — with talking. Like we used to.' She spoke with a note of desperation because she knew in her heart that what used to happen wasn't going to happen again. Not with Declan looking tempting and impossible on her bed.

'Fire away,' he said. 'What is it you want to talk about?'

'I don't know. Just — anything.'

'The weather?' he suggested.

Well, that should take all of a minute. Then maybe he would go. Why, oh, why, had she asked him in?

They discussed the weather, Kerry a little breathlessly, Declan in a bored drawl. Then he asked her about her bookshop, and when she told him how much she enjoyed running her own business, and how well it was doing, he seemed surprised, amused and a little skeptical. Kerry changed the subject to music before she was tempted to call him a patronizing jerk. Predictably, Declan favored classical and despised rock. When Kerry told him she liked U2 and R.E.M., he shuddered.

In the silence that followed, to her horror, Kerry heard herself asking, 'Declan, how come you've never married? It's not — not because of me, is it? I mean . . .'

What did she mean? How could it possibly be because of her that a man like Declan remained single? She stuck out her foot and pretended to be absorbed by her toes — which didn't prevent her from catching a glimpse of his smile — a cynical, disturbing smile that made her feel presumptuous and stupid.

'No,' he said. 'On that you can set your mind at rest.'

'Yes, of course. I didn't think you were pining for me or anything . . .'

Declan sat up. He appeared to be choking.

Kerry glared. 'What I *meant*,' she said, 'is that you strike me as the kind of man who would want a suitable sort of wife. I can even see you laying down the

167

law to a brood of well-mannered children. And I thought your experience with me might have — well, might have — '

'Left me with an incurable aversion to wedding bells?' He laughed softly, making her feel even more foolish.

Kerry drew herself up in her chair. Did he have to look at her with that taunting, catlike glitter in his eyes? If he was doing it on purpose to throw her off balance, it was working.

'Look,' she said. 'I'm sorry I brought it up. You're deliberately twisting everything I say. I'm just surprised you're not married, that's all. Now let's change the subject.'

'Not so fast,' said Declan. 'I'm not sure we've finished with this one.'

'I have,' said Kerry, who was hanging on to the sides of her chair to prevent herself from leaping up to kick him. That laid-back, mocking manner was either a self-protective shield or deliberate provocation. And she was becoming very tired of being provoked.

168

Declan shrugged. 'All right. As long as you've disabused yourself of the notion that I passed up the opportunity to marry on your account — '

'I didn't say that,' said Kerry, trying not to spit.

'Don't take it personally.'

'I won't,' Kerry snapped.

It wasn't true. She did take it personally. Oh, she didn't want it to be her fault that Declan had never married. Of course she didn't, if marriage had ever been what he wanted. But his flippant dismissal of even the possibility of her influence made her feel as if he'd stepped on her face.

She pulled awkwardly on the belt of her robe, only stopping when it became so tight she couldn't breathe. Or . . . She closed her eyes briefly. Was it the sight of Declan tossing off his jacket and making himself comfortable on her bed that was squeezing the breath from her lungs?

'What are you doing?' she gasped, as he bent down to unlace his shoes.

For answer, he settled his wide shoulders against the headboard and swung his legs onto the bed.

'Oh,' said Kerry despairingly.

Declan said nothing.

She closed her eyes. Dear Lord. Was he going to sit there for what was left of the evening, smiling like some inscrutable sphinx, while she fought a battle to the death with her libido?

'Why *haven't* you married then?' she blurted. She had to say something to take her mind off the magnificent body occupying her bed. Otherwise her mind was likely to stay stuck in a very risky groove.

'I thought we were finished with that subject.' Declan raked a hand through his hair. 'If you must know, I've never seen the point.'

He sounded brisk and indifferent — and yet there *was* something, an emptiness perhaps, that didn't quite fit with indifference.

'Companionship!' she suggested, reluctantly opening her eyes. She knew about loneliness. Surely even Declan could be lonely. And he had once seen a reason to marry her.

His mouth slanted cynically. 'I don't lack companionship when I want it.'

'Temporary companionship, you mean?' Kerry dug her fingers sharply into her palms.

'Mmm. Temporary suits me.'

'I see. And you've never felt a particular passion . . . ' She stopped. A blush was coming on. 'Never been in love,' she finished quickly.

'Love?' he said, as if she'd asked him if he'd ever robbed a bank. 'No, sweetheart, I haven't. As for a particular passion — yes, I've shared some very particular passions. On several occasions. Just as my parents share one for bridge. But I've never yet met a woman I could see myself spending my life with.'

To Kerry's blurred gaze his eyes seemed almost black in the dim light of the bedside lamp, and the words had an edge that cut deeply. She turned away so he wouldn't see the hurt he had inflicted. Hurt she knew she had no right to feel.

Silence fell between them. Then far away, on the edge of town, a wolf howled plaintively at the night. Its cry was taken up by another. And another.

'You were going to spend a lifetime with me,' Kerry said — and was appalled to hear a break in her voice. In case Declan had heard it, too, she made herself lift her chin and laugh.

He didn't laugh back. 'So I was,' he agreed softly. 'So I was.'

Kerry swallowed the lump in her throat. He'd sounded almost — grateful. As if he were thanking his lucky stars for his escape.

A moment later he confirmed her suspicion when he drawled, 'That, of course, was nothing more than youthful quixotry. You were in trouble — again, and more pressingly than usual — and I was foolish enough to think I should take you on.'

As if he'd been employing a new

kitchen maid who had turned out not to be satisfactory. Kerry forced her features to remain blank. 'Thank you,' she said.

'Thank you?' repeated Declan.

She nodded. 'Yes, indeed. It's such a relief to know you're not suffering from regrets.'

Declan smiled enigmatically and said nothing.

There was something about his smile that made Kerry long to take him by the shoulders and shake him. Instead, maintaining her façade of detachment, she crossed her legs so that the right one extended revealingly through the opening of her robe, and said in a voice that at first she didn't recognize as her own, 'But supposing we *had* got married . . . '

'I'd have made the best of it, of course.' Declan appraised the leg without visible emotion. 'Taken care of you and kept you out of trouble. Even if I had to lock you up and throw away the key.'

'That sounds like an odd sort of marriage.' Kerry pretended to be amused. 'Didn't it occur to you that there's supposed to be more to it than one partner riding herd on the other? You know, things like . . . ' She cleared her throat.

'Bed?' suggested Declan dryly. 'To be honest, I tried not to think about it. Cradle-snatching has never been one of my vices. Which is more than I can say for your Larry.'

Kerry's head snapped up. 'Larry was only three years older than I was. And I wasn't exactly a baby at the time.'

'To me you were.' She thought she heard a very faint sigh.

'Your mistake.' She gave a light laugh, damned if she would let him see how his words stung. He wasn't the only one who had tried not to think about bed. She glanced surreptitiously at his lean body draped across her covers — and tried not to think about it now.

His low baritone returned her to

174

reality. 'Mistake? I think not. Mind you, if I found myself in a similar situation today . . . ' His gaze stroked pensively over her blue velour robe, down the length of her bare exposed leg to the neat ankle, and then unhurriedly back up to her face. 'If it happened today, I believe I'd give the matter of bed *some* consideration.' He lowered his arms and this time his smile made her feel like Red Riding Hood discovering her grandmother had turned into a wolf.

Kerry pulled the folds of the robe hastily over her leg. He was only trying to get under her skin, of course. But how could it be that Declan — *Declan* of all people — was lying there on her bed making frankly suggestive comments and looking so alluringly masculine and desirable that she longed to hurl herself across the room and into his arms?

She stood up, pushing her hands deep into the pockets of the robe. It *must* have been too long since Larry. Far too long. But even that was odd in a way, because she hadn't been aware of any great deprivation until yesterday . . .

She took a deep breath. 'Are you suggesting — ?'

'Certainly not.' His tone was laconic. 'You're Kerry.'

'And that means — what?' She tilted her chin aggressively, daring him to insult her.

The corner of his mouth turned down. 'It means you needn't be afraid I'll touch you.'

'I'm not.' She laughed as though the idea were absurd. Then, incredibly, she heard herself asking, 'What if I touched *you*?'

To her dazed confusion, instead of tossing off some flippant rejoinder, Declan stiffened, and suddenly his eyes were hard as iron. 'Don't even think it, Kerry. I've shared passion and not much else with a few women over the years. With you I've shared more. I plan to leave it that way.'

Stunned by his harshness, Kerry put

a hand to her forehead. She flipped a lock of loose hair out of her eyes. So he wasn't interested. No surprise there. And of course she wasn't any more interested than he was. All she'd been suffering from was a case of temporary sexual frustration. It would pass. It had before.

'Don't worry,' she replied with a studied carelessness she found she couldn't feel. 'You wouldn't have been given a choice, you know. It was only an idle question.'

'Was it?' The look he angled her way glinted with a perception that disturbed her.

'Of course. I don't go around touching men just because they're there. Unless . . . ' She sat down abruptly. His thick, waving hair looked as if it belonged on her pillow. 'Unless I love them,' she finished, gazing distractedly around the room. At the walls, the pictures, the burn hole in the carpet. Anywhere but at Declan.

'Marriage didn't teach you a thing,

did it? You still believe in that sentimental nonsense.'

His voice was so bleak and flat that the urge to shake him became almost overpowering. 'Yes, I suppose I do,' she said. 'I'm not a total cynic like you.'

Odd. She hadn't realized it before, but she wasn't.

'Hmm.' He lowered his eyelids. 'How refreshing. So you still believe in the conventional charade.'

'Charade?' She twisted her belt and gazed glassily at the wall.

'What would you call it? Custom? Culture? Habit? The urge to procreate in order to ensure the survival of the species?'

'All those. But that doesn't mean there's no such thing as love between a man and a woman.' She wasn't sure why it was so important to convince him. Perhaps it had something to do with unresolved guilt.

'Doesn't it?' said Declan. He shrugged. 'I suppose you're entitled to your dreams. I'll leave you to enjoy them.' He swung his legs abruptly to the floor. 'Goodnight, Kerry. Oh, and don't sleep late. The ceremony starts at eleven, followed by lunch and a demonstration hockey game in the afternoon. Better dress warmly.'

Kerry blinked and rubbed a knuckle across her eyes. When she looked up, Declan was standing above her. His arms hung loosely at his sides, and he was frowning. She tried a tentative smile, and then watched in disbelief as, deliberately, he turned his back on her and made to leave the room.

'You've left your jacket,' she muttered.

Declan growled something under his breath, retrieved the jacket, and left again without looking back.

'Toad,' she snapped, just as he was closing the door.

She saw his fingers tighten briefly on the handle. Then he was gone.

Kerry stood up and threw herself on top of the bed. She could still feel Declan's warmth on the pillow. Damn. This trip, this whole Easter season, was turning out to be one giant mistake. But how in the world could she have known that Declan would turn up at just the wrong moment to take over her life as he had done so often in the past? Come to think of it, how could Lori *not* have known . . .

She sat up. Lori *had* known Declan was coming. She must have. The whole town knew. And Lori had always liked Declan, said he was right for Kerry . . .

Of course. That must have been the whole purpose behind this Easter invitation . . .

Kerry groaned and lay down again, turning her cheek into the fading warmth of the pillow. She caught the faint scent of Declan's skin. Damn Lori. She might have known the unexpected invitation had an ulterior motive. Her friend had always been an inveterate matchmaker. Well, this was one little scheme of hers that wasn't going to work — in spite of the indisputable fact that in the years since she had last seen Declan, he had changed from a magnetically compelling tyrant into a mouth-wateringly delectable man. A man who taunted her with his inaccessibility, and wore an almost visible 'No Trespassing' sign.

Kerry pulled the pillow over her head. What was it Declan had said? That he had never met a woman he'd want to share his life with? Not surprising for a man who thought love was a charade invented for the purpose of legitimizing sex.

She leaned over to snap off the light. If — and it was a big if — she decided to end her long celibacy, she wouldn't settle for less than a lifetime. Not again. If nothing else, her marriage to Larry had taught her exactly what she *didn't* want.

'I hate Declan,' she muttered into the darkness.

Nobody answered, except, in the distance, a lonely wolf. Several hours later she fell asleep.

When she woke up, someone was pounding on the door.

★ ★ ★

The new arena was a handsome gray brick building with dark red trim. Kerry's eyes widened as Declan led her into the freshly painted upstairs bar where those taking part in the opening ceremonies were gathered.

'Wow,' she exclaimed. 'Carmody Falls has never seen anything like this.' She waved at the bar, made of local amethyst, and at the smart black leather chairs on the marbled floor. 'No wonder they wanted you to see what your generosity had wrought. The rink's impressive, too. I love the red seats and — '

'Does this unexpected praise actually mean you've forgiven me for making you come?' Declan interrupted.

'Oh.' Kerry raised a hand to her mouth. For a moment she had forgotten that when she'd awoken that morning to find Declan pounding on her door, she had told him to go away and soak his head.

Declan hadn't gone away. He had informed her that if she didn't watch her tongue she could expect to find her own head under a tap. Then he had told her she was late.

Kerry replayed the scene in her mind.

'Late for what?' she'd asked, rubbing the sleep from her eyes as she opened the door just a crack.

'The opening of Carmody Falls' new arena. Hurry up, there's no time to waste.'

'But I'm not going to the Opening. I'm taking the bus to — '

'Kerry,' Declan pushed his way into the room and closed the door firmly behind him. 'Just for once in your life I'd like you not to argue. Now get dressed.'

'I will *not* — '

'You're not listening. Your assistant can manage the shop very well for another day or so. And I need you here.'

Kerry blinked. 'You *need* me?'

'That's what I said. I need you.'

'Why? Can't you find anyone else to boss around?'

Declan's chest expanded and he drew a long, controlling breath. 'Kerry, I don't want to boss you around. I'd much rather you came of your own free will. But long experience has taught me that *asking* you to do anything generally ensures you'll do the opposite. I haven't time for that kind of nonsense.'

Kerry sat down on the edge of her bed. 'Declan, can't you get it into your head that I'm not like that anymore? If you'd only tell me *why* you need me, I just might be willing to oblige.' She stared at the bare feet sticking out from under her robe. If Declan truly needed her — well, perhaps he was right that it was time she paid her debts. But she wasn't going to go meekly along with some stupid macho whim. Not without a reasonable explanation.

To her surprise, Declan turned his back on her and strode across to the window.

'Maybelle and Phil,' he said, staring

down at the street. 'I didn't find out how the land lay until I got here, and if I show up alone now . . . '

'If you show up alone now, Maybelle will latch onto you like an amorous wood tick,' Kerry finished for him. 'I see. And I suppose if it hadn't been for Phil, you'd have been quite happy to have Maybelle all over you?' She couldn't keep the acid from her voice, even though she could see Declan wasn't enjoying the role of visiting 'other man.' He hadn't even wanted to tell her why he needed her help.

He swung around, frowning, as if he was seeing her in a new and unfavorable light. 'An interesting turn of phrase,' he said. 'Yes, Maybelle's pretty enough in an overblown sort of way. I imagine we could have managed a pleasant weekend.'

'Pleasant,' jeered Kerry. 'Is that what you call sex?'

'Kerry,' Declan said warningly. 'What I call sex is none of your business. Now are you going to get dressed and come with me, or — '

'Or will you get the chance to play caveman again?' Her stomach gave a maddening little flutter at the thought, and she added hastily, 'No. Sorry to disappoint you. I'll come. For Phil's sake.'

'Thank you.' Declan gave her an exaggerated bow, then glanced at his watch. 'You have twenty minutes before we leave for breakfast.'

Just to show him she wasn't a pushover, Kerry took half an hour.

And now here she was at the arena. In spite of all her resolutions, Declan had won again. But she had to admit to feeling quite glad she'd come.

'I suppose I'll have to forgive you,' she said when she saw he was waiting for her answer.

'Good girl.' He smile was complacent, yet when he dropped an arm over her shoulder, Kerry felt an absurd thrill of happiness.

Until she saw Maybelle advancing in black and emerald splendor through the door.

7

'Declan!' cried Maybelle, holding out her hand and waiting with an expectant little smile until Declan took it. 'Our guest of honor. We *are* so pleased you could be here.'

Maybelle, in a busy green and black tweed suit, was doing her Councillor Welcoming Honored Guest routine — and doing it well, Kerry noted, with a feeling that was only partly amusement.

'Hello, Maybelle,' she said.

Reluctantly, Maybelle acknowledged her presence. 'Kerry. You're still here. I didn't realize you were staying for the big day.'

'Neither did I,' said Kerry.

The other woman's blue eyes darted sideways, seeking Declan's reaction. There wasn't one. With his hands in his pockets, he was gazing with apparent absorption at the arched beams supporting the ceiling.

'I understand the roads are quite passable now,' Maybelle remarked pointedly to Kerry.

'Yes,' Kerry replied. 'I believe they are.' Equally pointedly, she added, 'I was surprised to find Declan in town. Wasn't his connection with the new rink supposed to be kept under wraps?'

'Oh, but of *course* he was just being modest. Weren't you, Declan?' Maybelle batted her eyelashes and waited for Declan to look at her.

Kerry watched her with bemused fascination. She hadn't known people actually did that with their eyes outside of books.

'No,' replied Declan. 'I wasn't. I've never seen much virtue in false modesty.'

Probably true, thought Kerry. Declan wasn't excessively modest. On the other hand, she had never known him to push himself into the limelight. If he gave of himself or his assets, it was because he chose to. Not because he looked for recognition. In fact she had an idea excessive appreciation embarrassed him. It was the only damn thing that did, she realized with a certain resentment.

'Ladies. Gentleman.' Mr. O'Malley's voice cut off further conversation. 'Shall we proceed?'

Kerry stole a glance at her watch. Ten to eleven. Time for the production to begin.

She hung back as the official party headed for the door. As a mere guest, she didn't qualify to sit on the platform that had been erected at one end of the rink. But Declan, noticing her attempt to fade into the paneling, said at once, 'I've reserved a seat for you. In the front row.' He extended an elbow. 'Shall we go?'

Kerry frowned. 'Why? Did you think I might try to make a run for it?'

His eyebrows lifted a fraction. 'No. You're my guest, Kerry. As such, I want you front and center.'

'For Phil's sake?'

'Naturally.'

She sighed, without quite knowing why, and took the proferred arm with a quick straightening of her spine. But as Declan led her down the wide cement steps to join the chattering throng beside the rink, his leg brushed warmly against her thigh. Kerry drew in her breath sharply.

In that moment she made up her mind.

For this day only, she was going to forget her doubts, forget that she was only a decoy, and show the good people of Carmody Falls that she was proud to be Kerry Fleming, reformed teenage terror — the girl who had almost married Declan King and who, today, was proud to be his guest.

She lifted her chin, gave Declan a radiant smile, and allowed him to lead her to her seat.

Declan, on the receiving end of the smile, looked as if he'd been punched in the chest with a silk fist. He left her abruptly to join the party on the platform.

★   ★   ★

It could have been worse, Kerry decided an hour later.

The speeches had been brief and to the point — and Declan had held his audience with accomplished skill as he spoke of his youth growing up in Carmody Falls and his many happy memories of those years. Kerry noted with a mixture of pride and resentment that, as usual, he had the whole town at his feet.

'It is my great pleasure to be here with you today to declare this arena officially open,' he finished briskly, making no mention of his own contribution to the new rink and neglecting to use its official name — the King Arena.

Kerry made a face. She had been as hypnotized as anyone else by his magnetic presence on the platform, but she knew he *wasn't* especially pleased to be here. He wouldn't have come if it hadn't been for Maybelle's machinations and a disinclination to let down old friends.

Declan saw Kerry grimace, and sent her a repressive frown.

'Why the old-fashioned look?' she challenged him when he came to collect her for lunch. 'Did you think I was going to leap up and announce that you would have been much happier spending the day throwing your weight around the corridors of finance?'

'No,' he said. 'I thought you were going to make me laugh in the middle of Mayor O'Malley's speech.'

'Oh.' Kerry subsided. She'd almost forgotten Declan's quirky sense of humor.

After lunch there was a hockey tournament for which Declan was asked to drop the puck, followed by an Easter Pageant put on by the children from the figure skating club.

The Pageant proceeded quite tamely

until one little bunny began aiming rapid-fire Easter eggs at the fluffy chicken who had tweaked his white bob of a tail. When the chicken retaliated by emptying his basket of eggs over the bunny's head, the show degenerated into a free-for-all as bunnies, chickens and ducks scrambled chocolate eggs all over the ice and each other.

Kerry stole a glance at Declan, expecting to see restrained disapproval, but he was already in the thick of the melee along with a riot squad of harried coaches and fathers. Kerry was amused to see that he proved surprisingly adept at separating rival farmyard factions without the use of unnecessary force.

With audible sighs of relief, parents collected the combatants and everyone went home to get ready for the dance.

As the crowd shuffled outside, Kerry heard Maybelle say sweetly, 'You'll save the first dance for me, won't you, Declan? Of course I know everyone will be *dying* for you to ask *them* . . . '

'I certainly hope not,' said Declan,

looking poker-faced. 'I wasn't the Black Death last time I looked.'

Maybelle hit him playfully on the arm. 'Declan! How could you?' She giggled. 'What an awful thing to say.'

'He can do even better when he puts his mind to it,' muttered Kerry.

Declan's grip tightened on her arm. 'Time I took Kerry back to the hotel,' he said to Maybelle. 'Please excuse us.'

Maybelle opened her mouth, but before she could object, Phil had pushed his way out of the crowd and planted himself solidly in front of her.

'Can I drive you to the dance this evening?' he asked, reminding Kerry of a large dog waiting for a bone.

'Why, Phil, I don't know — '

'Great idea, Phil,' said Declan. He steered Kerry firmly in the direction of the Lincoln.

When she looked over her shoulder, she saw Maybelle attempting a gracious smile and Phil grinning with appealing adoration.

'Do you think he stands a chance?' she asked idly, as Declan maneuvered the car onto the street. 'Not that I can see why he wants one.'

'Sheath your claws, Kerry. Maybelle's very attractive in her way. Not to mention intelligent. As well as an excellent cook.'

'I'm surprised you're willing to pass up such a paragon,' Kerry said acidly.

Declan threw her a sardonic glance. 'You've got a point there. Maybe I shouldn't.'

Kerry sniffed and didn't bother to answer. But when he chuckled softly and patted her on the cheek, she felt as if all the years between had never happened, and she was once again as transparent as the child she had been when he first knew her.

She wouldn't mention Maybelle again. Declan was right. She *was* attractive and intelligent. He had every reason to admire her. And no reason whatever to respect the foolish girl who had left him at the altar.

★　★　★

The Decorating Committee had worked overtime to give the Town Hall a touch of glamour, and indeed the huge pots of greenery, the shaded lights and the band playing softly on the dais did lend it a more exotic air than usual.

Kerry and Declan arrived shortly after nine, following yet another hasty meal at Phil's. It had needed to be hasty because Phil was closing the café early in honor of the dance.

Maybelle, who was on the Welcoming Committee, was standing by the door waiting to greet them.

'Oh,' she said, eyeing Kerry's high-necked, blue silk dress with the long sleeves. 'What a sweet dress, Kerry. It suits you.'

'Thank you,' said Kerry, knowing that Maybelle, in backless and almost frontless red brocade, undoubtedly meant that it made her look like a schoolgirl. Earlier, she had decided to settle for demure in order to silence

Declan's gibes about her more sophisticated black dress. But he had made no comment when he'd fetched her from her room.

Now, watching him return Maybelle's eager smile, she decided he was quite capable of fending off unwanted advances without her help. If the advances *were* unwanted, which she wasn't wholly sure she believed. Whatever the case, she felt an immediate and pressing need to escape from the sight of Maybelle's mobile lashes.

'Excuse me for a moment,' she mumbled, and made her way quickly to the cloakroom.

When she returned to the hall ten minutes later, she found the band had begun to play in earnest. The dance was officially under way. And Declan was circling the floor with a clinging Maybelle wrapped in his arms.

Kerry fingered the flower-shaped gold brooch on her shoulder and tried hard to convince herself she didn't mind. Declan had every right to dance with whomever he chose. He had probably only insisted on her coming tonight because he still suffered from an irresistible urge to show her who was boss. As for the business about Phil . . .

Her thoughts were interrupted by a tentative tap on her right shoulder. She turned to find Phil gazing down at her beseechingly.

'Would you dance with me, Kerry? I know you're waiting for Declan — '

'No, I'm not,' said Kerry a little too emphatically. 'I'd love to dance with you, Phil.'

A moment later she found herself enveloped in a bear hug as Phil began to lug her around the floor as if she had no feet to call her own. After he had stepped on them three times in the space of a few seconds, she began to wish she hadn't.

'Sorry,' Phil muttered each time. 'Not my thing, dancing.'

Kerry was about to say that in that case she'd be delighted to sit out with him, when she discovered she was looking straight into Declan's eyes.

Maybelle's buxom body was pressed enticingly to his chest, and he was staring over her shoulder with a small, fixed smile on his lips. Just the same, Kerry saw that his hand was spread quite purposefully on her waist — and he was moving his hips in a way that instinctively made her swallow. She could imagine, vividly, what it must be doing to Maybelle.

But just as she was about to look away, she saw Declan detach his left hand from Maybelle's clutch and reach out to grasp Phil by the shoulder.

'My turn,' he said, moving Maybelle's still swaying body into Phil's welcoming arms, and in the same motion hauling Kerry into his. He conducted the whole operation with such smooth expertise that it was hard to tell how it had happened.

Wasting no time, Phil dragged a startled Maybelle to the other side of the hall. Kerry was left gaping up at Declan.

She was immediately conscious of his fingers splaying over her lower back, of the warmth of his breath on her hair, and of his subtle, irresistibly male scent. He held her close, moving with her as if the two of them were one, the hard pressure of his thighs sending pulsing, rapturous impulses through her veins, filling her with such an explicit longing that she lost all sense of control. If he released her she was certain she would fall.

Could this really be Declan? Her Declan — of whom she had always been slightly in awe, but whose affect on her had never been like this. Who had, on occasions, threatened to wallop her, but of whom she had never been genuinely afraid — not even when she had stood beside him at the altar and wondered what the coming night would bring.

She was afraid of him now. Not in a physical way, but as a man who could turn her world upside down by the mere pressure of his fingers on her waist — and the feel of his body moving against hers . . .

No. No, she couldn't allow him to overturn the world she had worked so hard to make secure. He had proved a hundred times already that to him she was no more than an endearing and exasperating adolescent. That wasn't, and could never be, enough.

'You deserted me,' she heard his deep voice murmur in her ear.

Kerry started. 'I went to powder my nose. Besides, you seemed to be managing very nicely without me.' She fixed her gaze on the deep crimson of his tie.

'Yes, I managed,' he agreed dryly. 'But now I expect you to do your job.'

'Job?'

'Mmm. I've had my obligatory dance with Maybelle. It's now up to you to monopolize me.'

'You didn't look obligated to me. You and Maybelle looked as cozy as bread and jam together.'

'I dance that way. In case you haven't

noticed.' He moved his hips so she couldn't fail to notice.

Kerry tried not to gasp. 'Maybe you do,' she said, shaken. 'But if you really want to pave the way for Phil, why don't you just *tell* Maybelle you're not available.'

'I have. Kindly. But short of calling her an unattractive cow, which she isn't, Maybelle isn't the sort of woman you can *tell* things. With Maybelle it's necessary to *show*. And if he's got any sense at all, Phil ought to be able to take it from there. She's always liked him as a friend and admirer.'

'Then why is she chasing after you?' Kerry knew she sounded catty and suspicious, but she couldn't seem to get control of her voice.

Declan laughed. 'Damned if I know. I'm the one who got away, I suppose.'

'Must be nice,' scoffed Kerry, as the beat of the music deepened and speeded up.

'What must?'

'Having endless women swooning at

your feet. No wonder your ego is so inflated.'

'Thank you. Not that my ego stands a chance with you around.'

He sounded more amused than insulted, and Kerry knew she ought to leave it go at that. But she couldn't resist taking it a step further.

'I couldn't dent your complacence if I tried, could I?' she said. 'It must be made of steel.'

'My point exactly. You're not swooning.' He swung her in a dizzying circle and bent her backward over his arm.

After a few seconds he pulled her upright again and, without thinking, Kerry gasped, 'No, but then you don't consider me a woman. Do you?'

All at once she felt his body tense. The music was throbbing up through the floor, but he stood quite still as the dancers whirled and circled around them. Someone bumped against her back. When he still didn't move, very cautiously she lifted her head.

His eyes were opaque, reflecting a

masklike blankness that made her skin prick. But when he saw her staring, he shook his head as if to clear it and said softly, 'Don't I? Would you *like* me to consider you a woman?'

Kerry swallowed. Was he serious? Or was that just his way of telling her he still saw her as a child? She studied his face, which wasn't masklike anymore, and tried to decide if those curving, sensuous lips had just issued a challenge, a rebuke — or something else entirely.

Whatever the case, she wasn't about to admit that maybe, just maybe, he had hit the nail on the head.

'No. Of course not,' she said. 'Why should I? I've never thought of you as a man.' She touched her nose, an instinctive gesture from childhood, in case the lie had made it grow longer.

'I see.' Declan narrowed his eyes. 'So I needn't hold my breath waiting for you to swoon. How disillusioning.'

The words were light, derisive. But he wasn't laughing inside. She could tell. He always spoke in that clipped, coolly amused tone when what he actually wanted to do was shake her.

Another body bumped into her back, and abruptly Declan swung her into a turn. After several more dizzying gyrations, he lifted an eyebrow and said, 'Well?'

'Well what?' she gasped, struggling to draw air into her lungs. 'If you mean am I going to swoon, the answer is no.'

'Good. Because I believe I left my smelling salts in Toronto.' His firm thighs pressed against her own, sending messages so precise that if he hadn't been holding her she would have fallen.

'Do stop acting like a toad,' Kerry snapped, when the strain became unbearable. She couldn't think of anything else to say.

His arm tightened around her. 'All right. How about I act like this?'

Before she could ask what he meant, he had tilted her head back and dropped a quick kiss on her forehead.

The music thundered to a crescendo

and stopped. Kerry pulled herself out of his arms.

'What was that for?' she gasped, knowing the heat that flamed deep within her must be reflected in the glowing scarlet of her cheeks.

He shrugged and gave her a small, enigmatic smile. 'Toads don't kiss. Men do.'

Kerry turned away. No, toads didn't kiss. Neither, apparently, did Declan. Not in any way that counted. She swept a hand through her hair, but when he caught it and would have drawn her into the next dance, she pulled away and darted for the door.

Behind her, somebody laughed. It sounded like Declan. She didn't stop to find out. The hall was full of people, and she had to get away — away from the heat, the laughter, the noise — and from Declan, to someplace where she could be by herself. Not to think. She was beyond thinking. But to breathe clean air and give the restless demons in her blood a chance to cool.

She ran to the cloakroom, grabbed her coat and hurried back into the hall. But just as she reached the front doors she caught sight of Maybelle. Maybelle saw her, too, and came hurrying up, dragging a beaming Phil by the hand.

'Kerry? You're not leaving? Have you and Declan had a falling out?'

'I don't think we ever had a falling in,' said Kerry. Then she took another look at Phil's besotted face, and remembered what Declan had said about Maybelle needing to be *shown*. 'No,' she amended quickly. 'We haven't had a falling out. As a matter of fact we've just become engaged.' Then she realized what she'd said, and nearly bit out her tongue. Lord, what had she done? Was she out of her mind?

'Again? I thought so.' Maybelle's unexpectedly cheerful voice penetrated the tumult in her brain. 'I suppose Declan has spent so much of his life looking after you he can't quite get out of the habit. Come on, Phil. Let's dance.'

Kerry was still groping for a response as Maybelle dragged Phil back on to the dance floor.

'Congratulations,' Phil called over his shoulder. 'That's great news. I — ' The rest of his speech was cut off as the two of them were swallowed up by the crowd.

Help, thought Kerry. Now what have I done? When Declan finds out, he'll . . .

She groaned and hurried out into the night.

The air was very cold and still now that it was no longer snowing, and the stars were bright points in the sky. She leaned against the wall and breathed deeply.

What had been going on in there? Declan, with his overwhelming sexuality, had almost knocked her off her feet with desire. But he hadn't taken her seriously. He never would take her seriously. Which meant she had to get away from him at once. Before he heard the lie she'd told Maybelle — and before she dissolved into a useless, quivering mound of frustrated hormones.

A taxi pulled up to let a young couple off at the curb. Kerry hurried toward it, but she had only made it halfway across the lot when she felt a heavy hand close on her shoulder.

'And where do you think you're going?' enquired Declan.

'Back to the hotel.' Kerry tried, unsuccessfully, to shrug him off.

'Oh, I don't think so.' His voice was drier than burnt toast. 'Especially as I've just been told we're engaged again.'

'We're not,' said Kerry. When he took hold of her other shoulder and pulled her against him so that she could feel his hard frame against her back, she drew a gasp of air and explained quickly, 'I just told Maybelle that so Phil would stand a chance. And I think it worked. So you see my job's done. And now I'm going back to the hotel to pack.'

She tried to pull away, but at once

Declan spun her around and grasped her upper arms, staring down at her as if he wanted to read her mind. Kerry watched his eyes in the glow of the streetlights. They were angry, hard. Then a shadow passed over his face, and when she looked again the hardness had been replaced by an emptiness that disturbed her far more than his anger.

'All right,' he said abruptly. 'I'll drive you. Wait in the car while I explain to the O'Malleys. I'll tell them you're not feeling well.'

Kerry blinked. 'But — '

'Don't argue, Kerry. As you say, you've done your job. So I'll make your apologies and take you back to the Cambrian. You can't leave alone at this time of night.'

'But — what about you?' This sudden reversal confused her, made her feel even less sure of what she wanted than before.

'What about me? I'll take you home and then come back to the dance. I owe that courtesy to the committee who invited me. You're under no such obligation.'

He sounded bored now, as well as irritated. And suddenly she hadn't the energy or the inclination to argue.

'Yes, OK, I'll wait,' she said as Declan unlocked the door of the Lincoln. When he gestured for her to get in, reluctantly she added, 'Thank you.'

He nodded noncommittally, shut the door behind her, and made his way back into the hall. Watching his tall figure stride across the lot as if he owned it, Kerry felt something tighten in her chest. He was such a beautiful man to look at . . .

Fifteen minutes later she was leaning on her windowsill at the Cambrian watching Declan's car pull away from the curb.

She stood there for some time, gazing blindly down at the street before she turned back into her room and began to throw clothes at her suitcase.

There had been no real reason for her to pack tonight, but it had been the first excuse that had occurred to her for running away from the dance — and from Declan. Dancing with Declan was like dancing on steaming hot coals. She couldn't have borne it again.

Kerry finished her packing and thought vaguely of phoning Lori to tell her friend what she thought of her matchmaking schemes. But in the end she decided to leave it until after she got home. Chicken pox wasn't fun. No need to make it worse.

Kerry made a face, and slowly peeled off the blue dress and donned her nightgown. Then she went to lie down on the bed.

She had been lying there for some time, before she realized she was waiting for the sound of Declan's car.

Tomorrow, of course, he would insist on driving her down to Thunder Bay. But could she let him? Kerry thought about that. It did seem only sensible. She could spend the night in a hotel and catch a plane to Winnipeg early the next morning.

After that she wouldn't have to think about Declan anymore — because he would be in Toronto, and she would be a thousand miles away.

Kerry stared at the blackness of the ceiling, waiting for that thought to bring her peace. It didn't — and it seemed a very long time before she heard the purr of an expensive engine below her window, followed, some minutes later, by the brush of a soft footfall outside her door.

She held her breath. Would he knock? If he did, would she let him in?

He didn't knock, and after a while she heard a key being fitted into the lock of the room next door.

If she had been asleep, she supposed she wouldn't have heard him switch on the TV and leave it on for some time. But she wasn't asleep, and she heard the TV, the shower and, eventually, what sounded like Declan doing push-ups.

When she finally drifted off to sleep it was to dream of pink crocodiles covering muscular male thighs.

★   ★   ★

The snowplows had been working overtime, and by the time Kerry and Declan drove out of town the next morning the roads were relatively clear.

They had maintained a wary and restrained civility over breakfast, Declan absorbed in his own thoughts, and Kerry trying desperately not to think. Thinking had become unaccountably painful. Fortunately, Phil had made up for their taciturnity with his beaming rhapsodies about Maybelle and the dance. It sounded as though the café owner was finally making progress with his suit.

The uneasy truce lasted only until they reached the turnoff on to the highway, where a group of children stood waiting to pelt the car with snowballs.

'Brats,' muttered Declan, slowing down. Glancing sideways, Kerry saw that his temper was on a very short leash. His eyes had a hollow, cavernous look about them this morning, and she guessed that he had slept lightly, if at all.

'Don't stop,' she said quickly. 'You can't put the whole lot of them across your knee.'

'And give me one reason why not?'

'Parents: Besides, you don't have the time. Just keep going. Faster.'

'That's your answer to everything, isn't it? Speed. If you had your way, I'd drive the whole way like a maniac at the wheel of a rogue tank.'

'No. But if I had my way you *wouldn't* drive like my Great Aunt Ernestine at the wheel of a golf cart.' Unfair, but he'd asked for it.

'You don't have a Great Aunt Ernestine,' Declan replied. But he didn't stop, and only one snowball hit the car.

Kerry smiled to herself. Declan

didn't *sound* riled, but she knew he was. Good. It was her turn for target practice today.

'I know I don't have an Aunt Ernestine,' she agreed. 'But if I had, you'd be driving just like her.'

Declan said something that sounded like witch, but was probably even less complimentary, and swung uncharacteristically fast around a corner.

Kerry folded her hands in her lap and stared straight ahead at the highway, which at this point was a quiet, uneventful stretch of road bordered by evergreens, birches and the distinctive Canadian Shield shale. The plows had done their job well, and the road surface was gritty with salt and sand between iced-gray borders of snow.

She managed to preserve her lofty silence until Declan, looking marginally less forbidding, pulled the car out of a turn, patted her knee and remarked that she was a pleasantly peaceful companion when she kept her mouth shut.

Kerry knew it was a trap to provoke her into losing her temper. She wasn't sure why Declan had awoken with the disposition of a cactus this morning, but she suspected he would only be content when he had reduced her to a similar frame of mind. Only she couldn't afford to lose her temper. She was having trouble enough dealing with the fact that his thigh was only inches from her knee.

'I'm glad you enjoy silence,' she said mildly. 'I do, too.'

'Good,' replied Declan, balked of his prey.

No more was said until they rounded a bend at a steady but unadventurous speed and came upon a tow truck, an upturned green van and something damp and lugubrious with eyes that looked like a grubby abominable snowman but was probably meant to be a dog.

Declan touched the brakes and skidded the car expertly to a stop. He hadn't much choice, because the tow truck was blocking the road.

'Great,' he growled. 'How do you feel about spending a night on the highway?'

'Not good. But surely it won't take long to move that van.' She glanced down both sides of the road. 'I wonder where its owner can have got to.'

Declan nodded at the dog. 'Maybe that lump of matted fur was driving.'

Kerry frowned. 'He looks gloomy enough. I wonder why they didn't take him with them.'

'Probably had the sense to recognize opportunity when it knocked.' When Kerry glared at him, he shrugged and said, 'Why don't you ask?'

Kerry studied the tow truck driver, who was busy hooking a grapple to the van. 'All right. I will.' She climbed out on to the crusted snow.

The dog, a large brown and white lump with thick paws, heavy jowls and short, floppy ears, gave her a look of such doleful gloom that she felt like flinging her arms around its neck.

'Will we have to wait long?' she asked the driver.

'Nah. Police have already been. Ambulance, too. Driver looked OK, but they took him into town to be sure.' He waved a hand at the van. 'Should have this heap out of here in a jiffy. Plenty more like it to keep me busy today. Bunch of idiots who don't know how to drive.'

Kerry looked back at Declan, who was lounging in his seat watching her with a cool little smile. Declan wasn't an idiot. But he thought she was.

'What about the dog?' she asked the driver. 'Is it yours?'

'Nope. Came with the van. Got left behind, I guess.'

'Oh. Are you going to take it into town with you then?'

'Nope. Got enough to do on a day like this without worryin' about no ugly old mutt.'

'Oh, but . . . ' She stopped. The man wasn't listening. He was getting on with his job. And the dog looked gloomier

219

than ever. She didn't think he was ugly. Just sad. And large.

She tramped back through the snow to Declan. 'We'll have to take the dog with us,' she told him. 'The tow truck driver won't, and the ambulance took its owner into town.'

Declan looked at her as if she'd suggested they load his car with pink elephants. 'No,' he said, and turned his attention to the controls of the Lincoln's radio.

Kerry narrowed her eyes and brushed a speck of sand off her nose. Then she walked across the road to the dog. It lifted its head, gave her a look of gathering gloom and sighed heavily.

'Don't worry,' said Kerry, patting it, and noting that 'it' was a 'he.' 'I'll take care of you.'

The dog rewarded her with a twitch of his long, feathery tail. She smiled, and walked back to Declan. 'We can't leave him,' she said, injecting all her powers of persuasion into the words. 'He might freeze. Or get run over.'

'Not likely,' said Declan. 'His owners will probably come back for him.'

'But what if they don't?'

'Kerry, it's not your problem.' She could hear the exasperation in his voice. 'If you're worried, we'll get in touch with the SPCA when we hit town.'

'Please — '

'I said no.'

Kerry turned away. She knew that tone. And that look. All hard, unbending and impervious to pressure. Declan wasn't about to change his mind.

And she wasn't about to leave that sad mat of fur beside the highway.

She turned around again, shoulders drooping, and blinked her eyelids very fast as she slid into the seat beside Declan.

He threw her an impassive glance, tightened his jaw, and went on adjusting the radio.

'The driver says we're going to be here for a while,' said Kerry in a voice that she hoped sounded meek and accepting.

Declan withdrew his attention from the radio. 'Did he say why?'

'No. I didn't think to ask . . . '

He muttered something she was fairly sure was unprintable, and swung himself out on to the road.

Tensing her body as if she were at the starting line of a race, Kerry waited until he was deep in conversation with the driver, then leaped out and skidded across the road.

'Come on, dog,' she whispered, grabbing him by the collar. 'Quick, before His High and Mightiness turns 'round.'

The dog, needing no second invitation, trotted obediently beside her as she hurried back to the car.

Swiftly she swung wide the back door and urged her new friend to climb in. Panting, he scrabbled his way on to the seat, scratched, and began to lick his lips.

Kerry caught just a glimpse of the blue-black fury in Declan's eyes as she squirmed into the passenger seat, slammed the door after her and locked it.

Then she sat back, closed her eyes and waited for the explosion.

8

Silence. Total, complete silence. Even the dog in the back seat seemed frozen into stunned immobility.

There was no explosion.

Kerry kept her eyes closed, but she was conscious of a shadow blocking out the sun, of a key being inserted in the lock and then of cold air stroking her skin.

'Look at me, Kerry,' said Declan.

Kerry looked at him. Cautiously. His carved mouth was only slightly flatter than usual, his jaw only marginally more rocklike. But when their eyes met, he said without inflection, 'Get out. Both of you.'

Oh, God. He honestly meant it. Kerry swallowed. Now what? She didn't want to grovel in front of Declan, but she *had* to make him agree to take the dog.

'I'm sorry,' she said, trying not to sound defensive. 'But you see, I couldn't just leave him by the road.'

Declan's mouth began to resemble a granite slab, and his blue-black gaze traveled over her as if he were contemplating the pros and cons of murder. 'No,' he said. 'I don't see. I said get out.'

Kerry pinned her gaze resolutely on his face. 'I know you did. Are you planning to leave *me* beside the road, as well?'

Declan paused in the act of reaching for her arm. He closed a gloved hand over the top of the door. Kerry watched him take a deep breath and then exhale with a quick rush of air. 'I don't know what I was planning,' he said after several tense seconds. 'But you wouldn't have liked it. And no, I don't propose to leave you beside the road.'

Kerry licked her lips. They felt cold. 'I'm not leaving the dog,' she said quietly. 'I couldn't live with myself if I thought he mightn't be looked after.'

Declan scowled and slammed his fist on the roof of the Lincoln. Kerry pressed her feet to the floorboards and waited, expecting at any moment to be hauled out onto the hard-packed snow. But in the end all he said, in a grating, barely controlled voice, was, 'I know the feeling. If I didn't, I'd have had sense enough to leave *you* behind in Carmody Falls.' After a pause, he added, 'All right, the dog stays. For now. You, I'll settle with later.'

'Thank you,' Kerry said, meaning it.

Declan didn't get behind the wheel at once. Instead he walked back to the tow truck to hold a brief conversation with the driver. When he returned to the car he was swearing. Kerry eyed him warily as he peeled off his gloves, slapped them against his thigh, and sat down. The dog leaned over the seat and ran a grateful tongue across her cheek.

'It's planning to have you for supper,' said Declan, sounding as though he was talking through his teeth. 'Too bad it's going to have to wait till I'm through with you.'

Oh, dear. She didn't like the sound of that.

But she'd won her point. There was no sense in further ruffling Declan's feathers — for all he did look astonishingly delectable with his winged black brows drawn together and his eyes all fire and black ice.

'I'm sure it was a mistake,' she said placatingly. 'His owner is bound to want him back. I mean, how could he possibly not?' She turned to run her hand down the dog's muzzle. The dog promptly wiped his tongue along the back of Declan's neck.

'Do you want me to answer that?' asked Declan.

Kerry took one look at his face and decided she didn't.

A minute or two later the tow truck righted the van and pulled it to the side of the road. As there were no other cars ahead of them, in a few seconds they were once again on their way to Thunder Bay.

Kerry maintained a cautious silence for the next fifteen minutes, but when she saw the deepening lines of weariness around Declan's eyes, she remembered thinking that he probably hadn't had a lot of sleep.

'I'll drive, if you like,' she offered, trying to make amends for the dog. 'You look tired.'

'I am,' said Declan. 'Of coping with the idiotic antics of one of the most aggravating females I've ever had the misfortune to meet up with. And no, you won't drive.'

'And give me one reason why not.' Kerry forgot all about making amends.

'Only one? All right, how about because you're an incorrigibly reckless driver with a juvenile passion for speed.'

'I am not.' A flatbed truck loaded with plywood was approaching on the other side of the highway, so she resisted an immediate urge to punch his nose. 'I'm an extremely skillful driver who knows how to get where I'm going.'

'That's exactly what I'm afraid of,' said Declan. 'However, this is not my vehicle, and I have no plans to die before my time.'

'That remark is totally uncalled for, and you know it,' Kerry snapped, suddenly determined to win this battle. 'Go on, move over. I can't drive sitting in your lap.'

Declan shook his head as if she'd suggested he dose himself with arsenic. 'You amaze me sometimes,' he remarked. 'If memory serves, driving from people's laps was exactly the sort of thing you used to do routinely.'

He *was* in a bad mood. 'Not people's. Just Larry's. You're not Larry.'

'For which small mercy we may both yet be truly thankful.' Declan's fulminating gaze remained riveted on the road.

Kerry doubted it. Larry had never been such a stick-in-the-mud about her driving. And she didn't even want to think about sitting in Declan's lap. She touched his arm and gave him what she hoped he would interpret as a reassuring smile. 'Don't worry, I'll be very careful.'

'You don't know the meaning of the word.'

All thought of conciliation vanished. 'You mean you've cornered the market on caution?' she taunted.

If she'd hoped to dent his self-assurance, the attempt failed. Declan only smiled grimly and continued to drive with consummate skill and without breaking a single rule of the road.

They drove the rest of the way without speaking, although every now and then the silence was broken when the dog leaned over to nuzzle Declan's ear, and Declan responded with two or three succinct phrases prominently featuring the word 'broomstick'.

Kerry was careful not to respond.

When they reached Thunder Bay, Declan drove straight to the Fort

William side of town and pulled up outside a two-story house on North Harold Street.

'What are we doing here?' Kerry asked suspiciously.

'Unloading that hairy horror in the back. The tow truck driver gave me the owner's address.'

'Oh.' Kerry just had time to nod before a thin woman holding a Siamese cat appeared on the doorstep.

'I understand this is your dog,' said Declan, getting out.

The woman shook her head. 'Not ours. My brother-in-law's.'

'In that case you'll be wanting him back.'

'Not on your life. He's dead.'

Declan turned a bleak eye on the dog, who was sitting up in the back seat with his ears on end and a hopeful eye fixed on the cat. 'He's not dead. He's thinking up recipes for Siamese stew.'

The dog licked his lips.

The woman frowned. 'I didn't mean

Barker was dead. My brother-in-law is.'

'Barker?'

'The dog. That's his name. Steve was crazy about him. But Steve got himself killed in a brawl. Good riddance, I say. Except we got stuck with the damned dog. My husband was going to take him to the pound.'

Barker stopped licking his lips and sighed.

'Oh, but he can't do that,' exclaimed Kerry. 'What if the pound can't find him a home?'

'Huh. Don't suppose they will. Who'd want a monster like that?'

'I would,' said Kerry promptly — and instantly became aware that Declan was looking at her as if he'd like to install her in a particularly uncomfortable padded cell without possibility of release for ten years.

'Don't be any more of an idiot than you have to be,' he said coldly, turning back to the woman with the cat. 'Madam, I'm afraid Barker is *not* my responsibility. You'll have to take him.'

'But she'll send him to the pound,' wailed Kerry.

'Rather her than me,' said Declan. 'Come on, Barker. Out you get.'

Barker looked up at him with brown, soulful eyes and offered a paw.

Kerry watched a couple of stray snowflakes drift down from a tree and settle in Declan's hair, and saw that the time had come for desperate measures — even if they did make her look like a sniveling fool.

She dashed a hand over her eyes, gave a small, calculated sniff and began to grope in her pocket for a tissue.

'Cut it out, Kerry . . . ' growled Declan.

She sniffed again and dabbed furiously at her eyes. Barker offered the other paw.

Declan swore and got back into the car, looking as if he was thinking of taking up homicide as a sideline.

Kerry gave him a dazzlingly grateful smile. 'Thank you,' she said. 'I knew you wouldn't let him go to the pound.'

Declan pulled on his gloves and gripped the wheel. He didn't speak for several seconds, and when he did it was in a low, close-to-explosive voice that made Kerry pull as far away from him as she could.

'Kerry,' he said, 'there's something you need to get straight. I am not a fool. I never have been — and I've known you far too long to be taken in by phony tears and a pair of baby blue eyes. And so help me, if you try any more of your nonsense on me, I'll — '

'I won't,' said Kerry hastily. 'I am sorry about Barker, really I am, but — '

'But you'd do it again in an instant,' finished Declan, flicking on the ignition. 'If you thought it would help you get your way.'

'But *you're* the one who always gets his way.'

'Am I? I suppose that's why my upholstery currently smells like wet dog.'

'You could have said no,' muttered Kerry.

'To the best of my recollection, I did say no. For which piece of perfect good sense, a car which doesn't belong to me has been turned into a mobile zoo. And for which, my girl, you are sooner or later going to pay.'

'Idle threats,' scoffed Kerry, who was only capable of carrying gratitude so far.

All the same, she wondered if he meant it. Declan had never been one to let her get away with much, and in this case she couldn't altogether blame him. She'd had no choice but to get away with Barker though. On that score she hadn't a doubt. And if a fondness for dogs and a contempt for unkindness to animals made her a thoughtless adolescent in Declan's eyes — well, that was just too bad. She should be used to his disapproval by now.

Should be. And yet his censure continued to rankle. Frowning, she adjusted the strap of her seatbelt. Maybe it was Phil's duck-egg sandwiches, eaten in rigid silence along the way, that were at the root of the sinking feeling in her stomach. It was the only explanation that made sense.

Barker woke from a short, refreshing nap as Declan was turning the car onto Memorial Avenue. When a passing pedigree peke reminded him that it was time to inform the inhabitants of Thunder Bay he'd hit town, he opened his mouth and began to bark in a deep, rumbling roar.

'Shut up, Barker,' said Kerry.

Barker went on justifying his name.

'Barker,' said Declan warningly.

That was all it took. Barker shut.

Damn him, thought Kerry. Why does even the dog do as he orders?

She opened her mouth to ask him, then was struck again by the deep navy shadows beneath his eyes.

He really was tired. Of putting up with her, most likely. As he had also, however reluctantly, agreed to put up with Barker. When the chips were down, Declan had always come through for her, sometimes at considerable cost to himself. She ought to be grateful. Was grateful.

'Declan . . . ' Impulsively Kerry reached out to touch him, wanting to let him know that she wasn't unaware of what she owed him. As the nearest part of him happened to be his thigh, she patted that.

The Lincoln swerved, skidded over a small, gray snowdrift, and made straight for a large blond lady carrying a muff.

If Declan had been a less experienced driver, he would almost certainly have run the blond lady over. As it was, he managed to wrestle the car back on course. The muff, which turned out to be a poodle, started to bark.

Barker barked back enthusiastically, and the altercation continued until they rounded the next corner.

The knuckles of Declan's left hand whitened on the wheel as he pulled the car to a stop by the curb. 'Kerry,' he growled, extending an arm along the back of the seat and winding her hair tightly around his fist. 'Don't you have sense enough to know that interfering with the driver is dangerous? Could even prove fatal?'

Kerry gulped. She could feel his fingers bunched against her neck. 'Sorry,' she said. 'All I did was put my hand on your — '

'I know exactly what you put your hand on,' Declan said roughly. 'And if you do it again you're likely to find my hand on a part of you in a way you won't like.'

'You're getting disgustingly bad-tempered in your old age,' Kerry complained. 'You never used to mind — '

'Well I mind now. Just remember that as long as you're in my car.' He jerked the engine back into gear.

'No problem,' she scoffed. 'I think I may survive the deprivation.'

What in the world was eating him now? Why was he behaving as if his admittedly delectable body was some kind of sacred vessel too valuable for mere mortals to touch? Arrogant jerk. Did he really think every woman he met was panting to put her hands all over him? Even if a lot of them were.

She was too irritated to speak as they followed the road to the Port Arthur side of town. But as they traveled the length of Cumberland Street, and the silence between them continued, irritation faded, and an odd lump began to form in her throat. She had never touched Declan in that way. Not even when he had asked — no, *told* her to marry him. On that memorable occasion she had stood meek and bewildered while he gave her a quick peck on the cheek, patted her absently on the head, and told her she'd have to behave herself from now on.

She slanted a quick look at his face. It was as stern and unrevealing as ever. Nothing had changed. So why was he behaving as if he suspected her of trying to seduce him in a moving vehicle on a slippery street at the tail end of an exceptionally heavy snowstorm?

Probably just habit, she decided.

Declan had become an enigmatic, disturbingly sexy man. He was also dictatorial, opinionated and disapproving, and he had long ago acquired the annoying habit of telling her what to do.

He wouldn't be doing it much longer. Involuntarily, she released a soft sigh.

A sign that read, *Amethyst Mine Next Left*, caught her eye, snapping her instantly back to her surroundings. Had she really been so busy dreaming that she had failed to notice they were on the highway out of town?

'Declan? Where are we going?' she demanded. 'We're nowhere near the airport. I planned to spend the night in Fort William — '

'No need. My old friend, Harry, lives just up the road. Remember him?'

'Yes, of course I do. He — he was going to be your best man, but — '

'Mmm. He was. Now he practices law in Thunder Bay.'

'So — ?'

'So he's gone to Minneapolis for a

week, and he's offered me his house for the night.'

'That's nice. But I'm not staying with you in anyone's house. Please stop the car at once.' Kerry spoke in her most imperious tones, even though her insides felt like jelly. She *couldn't* spend another night with Declan. She just couldn't.

To her surprise and relief, he slowed down at once and pulled the car up beside an attractive red brick pub called the King's Moose. It was nestled among a grove of maples, and through the bare branches Kerry could just see the icy shores of Lake Superior.

'OK,' said Declan. 'Now what?'

'I'm sorry, but I'm afraid you'll have to take us back to Fort William.'

'Mmm-hmm. You were planning to spend the night at the dog pound, were you? I'm sure they'll provide you with clean straw.'

'Oh.' Kerry put a hand to her mouth. 'Barker.'

Behind them, Barker thumped a sleepy tail.

'Precisely,' said Declan dryly.

'The hotels won't take him, will they?'

'Not if they value their continued prosperity.'

'He's not *that* bad,' objected Kerry. When Declan only looked at her with a familiar grim twist to his mouth, all at once she was overtaken by a wave of such unexpected desolation that she heard herself saying wretchedly, 'I'm causing you trouble again, aren't I? You'd like to be rid of me, but all because of Barker you're stuck.' She bent her head and smoothed a hand over the fabric of the seat.

Just for a moment she imagined she felt Declan touch her hair. Then, because she couldn't think of anything more to say, she began to grope for the handle of the door.

9

'Kerry.' Declan's voice was gruff, exasperated. 'Kerry, I didn't say I wanted to be rid of you. I think I can survive the aggravation for one more night.'

Kerry went on searching blindly for the handle, then bent forward to press her head against the window.

Declan muttered something that didn't sound complimentary and closed his hand on her shoulder. When she resisted, he growled some more and pulled her around to face him.

'Kerry,' he said flatly, 'you could have caused an accident back there. If that's what this is about, you can forget the dramatics because you deserved every word I said to you. Outside of that, if I've been hard on you — I'm sorry.'

Sorry? He didn't sound it. He sounded impatient. 'You were just being yourself,' she said dully.

Declan's tanned skin pulled tight across his cheekbones. 'Is that so? You're certainly right that having the Hound from Hell inflicted on my upholstery hasn't done a lot to improve my temper. Can you think of any reason why it should?'

'No,' she admitted, twisting the seat belt around her fingers. 'It *wasn't* fair of me. That's why it's time I got us both out of your hair. And your car.'

Declan sighed and began to knead her shoulder through the fabric of her jacket. 'Kerry, don't be more of a dimwit than usual. It isn't like you to run away from trouble.'

Kerry's laugh came out sounding like a croak. 'Trouble? You're certainly that.'

He stopped kneading and bunched his knuckles under her chin. 'If either of us is trouble, sweetheart, it's you. And if you want me to keep my sanity and my temper, you'll call a halt to these unnecessary jitters, and trust me to get us through the night without either seducing you or resorting to some tempting but sadly illegal violence.'

This time he did sound as if he meant it. Kerry looked up quickly, and at once he moved his hand to the back of her neck.

As his fingers tangled in her hair, she thought she heard him murmur something that could have been, 'Trouble and honey-blond silk.'

What on earth was he talking about? She wanted to pull away, but her limbs felt heavy, lethargic.

After a moment Declan drew her face on to his shoulder.

She rubbed her cheek against the smoothness of his parka. It smelled clean with the fresh tang of winter. When, after a while, she lifted her head, her mouth was only inches below his chin.

The pupils of Declan's eyes darkened, and as Kerry sat there, mesmerized, he leaned forward and brushed his lips across her mouth.

Lightning sizzled through her veins.

She tensed, waiting for the magic to continue. In the same moment Barker started to pant noisily in the back seat. When Declan swore softly, Kerry gave a little gasp and pulled away.

She pinned her gaze on the intense bright glitter of his eyes.

Surely that feather-light contact couldn't be counted as a kiss? Yet suddenly every cell in her body had come alive, responding to his nearness, to the warmth of his skin — to his fingers in her hair, his thumb gently teasing her neck. Heat flared and welled up in her from nowhere, bathing her in a warm pool of longing. At first it was formless, then for a few seconds Declan was the focus of her world.

She wanted him as she had never wanted Larry.

But Declan was Declan. He was looking at her now as if he wondered who she was and how she had strayed into his arms. Arm really. His right one was resting on the wheel. Which meant that what, for her, had been a revelation, for him had been no more than the old impulse to comfort little Kerry in distress.

He released her with an abruptness that made her gasp. 'Right. Nonsense over, I hope?' He raised his eyebrows in a way that was more command than question.

Kerry nodded. She was too dazed, too shattered to argue. And she had temporarily forgotten what, exactly, they had argued about.

Ten minutes later, after a short drive along the lake-shore, Declan swung the Lincoln off the road and drew to a halt in front of a low, cedar-frame house perched near the edge of the water.

Kerry scrambled out. She didn't want Declan's help. She was afraid of what would happen if he touched her.

Lingering memories of the kiss-that-hadn't-been-a-kiss floated, dreamlike, through her mind. She and Declan hadn't spoken since that electric moment near the King's Moose, and she had spent the time trying to understand the significance of her body's startling and continuing reaction to the powerful pull of Declan's masculinity.

So far she had come to no conclusions that made sense.

As Declan made his way up the path, Kerry watched the last rays of the sun skimming pale and insubstantial across the lake. In places the ice was transparent, already starting to melt.

Winter was on its way out.

She took a long breath of cold evening air, and looked around her. The last snowfall had left a glittering winter wonderland in its wake. Delicate fingers of lace lay on the trees, and the roof of Harry's house was a smooth white blanket trimmed in faded gold.

Reluctantly, Kerry tore her gaze from the scenery and followed Declan.

'I'll need my own room,' she warned him, after navigating the narrow path Harry had cleared to the front door. 'They've probably only prepared one for you.'

248

'Good. We're in agreement.' Declan's reply was laconic and unflattering. 'And knowing Harry, we'll be lucky if he's prepared clean linen. By the way, you get to sleep with the dog.'

Barker grunted and sat down on Declan's feet.

'Furry menace,' he muttered, bending down to pick up a piece of paper that had been slipped under a rock beside the doormat.

'*Help yourself to food, drink, bed, fire, anything you need except Fiona. She's with me. Sorry to miss you. Harry.*'

'Who's Fiona?' asked Kerry.

'Harry's girlfriend. And no, he wasn't serious. I don't dabble in other people's women.'

'I should hope not,' Kerry scoffed. Then without thinking, she ran a hand over Barker's head and added vaguely, 'Especially as I'm sure you don't need to.'

'Why thank you, Ms. Fleming. That's the nicest thing you've said to me all day.'

Kerry straightened at once, only to encounter a mocking grin and a double dose of highly charged eyepower.

'I wasn't thinking,' she said quickly. She still wasn't. It was impossible to think when Declan looked at her like that. She knew he was teasing, but it still turned the lining of her stomach inside out.

He gave a short laugh and pulled a key from behind a planter next to the door. 'Weren't you? Why am I not surprised?'

Kerry was still trying to come up with a rejoinder when he put a hand on her shoulder and urged her into a large, bright hallway decorated in cheerful shades of autumn. A big bowl of rushes stood on a table beneath a wide bow window. The effect was warm, welcoming and, because she was alone with Declan, unbearably disturbing and unsettling.

'Welcome to my parlor,' said Declan.

Kerry pulled away from him and went to stand with her back to the wall.

'It's not your parlor. It's Harry's.' She had to say something to put him in his place, even if it did sound ridiculous.

'So it is. But since Harry's not here, you'll just have to settle for me.'

'As resident spider?' she asked — then wished she hadn't, because he had been speaking in that burnt-toast voice again. And he was smiling, not like a spider, but like a particularly sensuous cat in pursuit of a mouse.

She stared at him, hypnotized.

He took a step toward her, and there was a gleam in his eye she didn't trust. But all at once he stopped short. The gleam faded and turned dark — as if he'd set his sights on a mouse that had turned out to be a beetle, Kerry thought wildly.

He looked incredibly alluring in his tightly molded jeans, with the black sweatshirt he was wearing beneath his jacket stretched across the breadth of his chest. She wondered what he was thinking. But the slight frown between his eyebrows gave no clue. Then abruptly he threw off the jacket, flung it over the table with the rushes, and said, 'Right. Let's see what Harry's left us to eat.'

Barker, who had followed them in, wagged approvingly at the mention of food.

Harry, as it turned out, had left nothing. A pot of what had presumably been soup sat thick and unappealing on the stove, but the polished pine table bore nothing more edible than crumbs. A pile of dishes, grimy with the decaying remains of food, lay in the sink daring them to approach.

'You do the dishes,' said Declan. 'I'll find us something to eat.' He pulled open the fridge and bent down to investigate the contents.

'Coward,' said Kerry.

'I beg your pardon?'

'I said coward,' she repeated. 'You can't face those slimy looking dishes, so you're leaving them to me.'

'What I actually can't face,' said Declan, straightening, 'is the prospect of sitting down to a supper that tastes like boiled socks. I have an excellent memory, sweetheart. So you do the dishes.'

'Declan King, just because I wasn't much of a cook seven years ago doesn't mean I can't cook now. I've had a lot of practice since then.'

'Mmm. Is that so? How long did you say you'd been married when Larry left you?' Declan smoothed a hand along his jaw.

'Oh! Of all the rude, ill-mannered *toads*, you . . . ' She paused to gather steam. 'Declan, how dare you try to blame Larry's leaving me on — on — '

'Your cooking?' He closed the fridge and leaned against it with his arms crossed. 'OK, so you didn't drive him away with sacrificial pork chops or sardines. I'm still not letting you do the cooking.'

Kerry suspected Declan was provoking her purely to punish her for Barker. But she couldn't seem to stop herself from rising to the bait.

'It's not up to you,' she snapped. 'I don't have to take orders from you. Not anymore.'

'Did you take them from Larry?'

Kerry wondered why, all of a sudden, there was a funny, flat, look in his eyes. How had Larry got mixed up in this conversation? She didn't want to think about Larry — who hadn't been remotely like Declan.

'No, I did not,' she replied. 'Besides, giving orders wasn't his way. He just blustered.'

'And a fat lot of good it did him. That's why I'm *telling* you to get on with the dishes.'

'Really?' Kerry felt all her muscles stiffen. 'That's too bad, isn't it? Because I've decided to leave them to you.'

'Have you now?' He was across the room in seconds without even seeming to hurry. Then, before she could take in what was happening, he was behind her, and she found herself being propelled smartly in the direction of the sink.

She dug her heels into the white-tiled floor — and Declan slammed up against her back.

Mistake. Big mistake. She could feel his body, lean, hard and seductive, invading her senses and paralyzing her will to resist. Except that it wasn't his body she needed to resist.

It was the damn dishes.

He pushed her forward again, his legs pressing against hers, forcing them to march. When she found herself up against the sink, it came to her that she was locked in a power struggle that, for some inexplicable reason, had more to do with Larry and the past than it had to do with a sinkful of dirty dishes.

Which made no sense. Declan had no need to prove he was a better man than Larry.

Kerry closed her eyes. Now where had that thought come from? Declan was an autocratic, exasperating, over-controlling corporate hunk — who, years ago, had shown great compassion to a confused and insecure little girl.

'Declan, what's this all about?' she asked, gripping the edge of the sink. 'Why does it matter who does the dishes? And what does it have to do with Larry?' When she felt him loosen his grip, she turned around.

He was frowning, and his mouth had gone all straight and traplike. Across the room, Barker was staring fixedly at the fridge.

'It matters who does the dishes mainly because I value my digestion. And I'm damned if I'm doing all the work while you sit on your charming little fanny filing your nails.' He paused. 'And it has nothing to do with your deplorable Larry.'

Kerry glared. 'Then why bring him up?'

He shrugged. The lines beside his mouth were sharply etched. 'No good reason. Although I shouldn't have allowed you to marry him.'

'You couldn't have stopped me.'

'Oh, yes, I could.' He closed his hands on the sink, trapping her between his arms so she couldn't move.

'Well . . . ' Kerry squirmed uncomfortably. If only he wouldn't stand so *close*. 'I suppose you could if — if I'd thought you really cared. You didn't though, did you?'

'What do you think?' He spoke as if he were sharpening a knife on her nerve ends.

'I don't know. For a minute there you were acting just the same way Larry did. All male and possessive — but really more interested in your stomach.'

Declan's eyes narrowed. 'Hardly. If you were mine, Kerry Fleming, I promise you I wouldn't walk out on you.'

'Oh, I know you wouldn't.' Impulsively she put her hands on his shoulders. But he removed them at once and drew back.

Kerry frowned. 'I take it back,' she said sharply. 'At least Larry didn't retreat into his shell like a snail the moment I touched him.'

'A snail?' said Declan. 'You think I'm a snail?'

'Or maybe a tortoise.' Kerry ignored the faint menace in his tone.

Declan shook his head as if he thought she'd taken leave of her senses.

Kerry glowered. What did he think she was? A virus with a low IQ? She felt her control snap like a brittle rubber band, and without pausing to think of the consequences, she raised her arms and wrapped them around his neck. She'd show this arrogant, hurtfully magnetic man she was no virus.

He didn't respond, so she gave him a slow, sensuous smile and began to rotate her hips in a leisurely, voluptuous motion against his body.

He reacted then — so quickly she hadn't time to gasp. One moment she was on her feet enjoying a pleasantly erotic connection with his athletic frame. The next she was half sitting, half lying across the kitchen table and Declan was looming over her with his fists on either side of her hips. Then his mouth was on hers, firm, crushing, efficient, pressing her head back until she was forced to hold on to him for balance. The heat she had felt earlier in the car flared up harder and brighter than before. It started in her toes and soared upward like a dangerous flash fire. When it reached the top of her head and she was sure she was about to explode, he straightened, ran his hard hands deliberately over her hips and let her go.

He was breathing only a little faster than usual, but his eyes were blue fire lighting the sharp angles of his face. 'Well?' he said. 'Want to go out and kiss a snail? Or a tortoise?'

Hadn't he felt *anything*? Had that kiss, a real one this time, been nothing more than an exercise in power? Gradually the flames of unsatisifed passion started to die down, and Kerry saw that, incredibly, Declan's mouth had softened, the edges begun to tip up.

Not power then? Only a joke? Kerry sagged back against the table.

She tried to smile. No point letting him know what his kiss had done to

259

her, that he had just turned her world upside down.

No point wanting what she knew she could never have.

'No thanks,' she said. 'No snails. It would be an anticlimax after kissing a toad.'

For a moment she wondered if she'd gone too far. But after a brief, disbelieving silence, Declan threw his head back and let out a crack of laughter. 'Trust little Ms. Fleming to keep me from getting a swelled head.' He eyed her pensively, then said in a different, more abrasive tone, 'I suppose it didn't cross your mind that if you kiss the right toad, he sometimes turns into a handsome prince?'

Was he serious? As usual with Declan, it was impossible to tell. She eyed him warily, unsure of her own feelings beyond the obvious — and not anxious to make herself any more vulnerable than she already was.

'You didn't give anything time to cross my mind,' she told him. When he frowned, she added, 'I suppose you're handsome enough. But I don't think they make corporate princes.'

'You little . . . ' Declan started to reach for her, then let his arms drop as if he didn't trust himself to touch her. 'Watch it, sweetheart. Remember — you're alone with an experienced corporate toad.'

There was a definite threat in the softly spoken words. But Kerry was in no mood to hear it. 'And a furry fridge magnet,' she corrected him, gesturing at Barker who still had his nose pointed at the fridge.

'How could I forget?' Declan ran a hand around the back of his neck, glowered at the top of Barker's head, then asked curtly, 'How do you propose to transport that deranged doormat back to Winnipeg? Because if you think I'm driving the two of you one kilometer further than the airport, you're — '

'I don't,' Kerry said quickly. 'I'll arrange to have Barker shipped.'

Barker sighed. Declan glanced at him and said nothing. But Kerry didn't miss his swiftly contained smile.

After that the evening passed without overt friction, although with a certain wary tension on Kerry's part. If Declan felt a similar reserve, it didn't show.

At his terse suggestion, in the end they compromised and did the dishes together. Later, he watched skeptically as she began to whip up Eggs Florentine. But when they turned out to be not only edible but appetizing, he was magnanimous enough to apologize for maligning her cooking.

Kerry smiled smugly and was magnanimous enough not to say, 'I told you so.'

When supper was over, Declan lit a fire and they sat on either side of it reading the papers and trying to pretend the other one wasn't there. At least Kerry was trying to pretend she wasn't conscious of every slight movement of his hands as he thumbed through pages of news and settled down to peruse the financial section. She still had no idea what he was thinking. But for her, the kiss they had shared seemed to hang in the air like a question mark, adding to the tension that had never been far from the surface since they had first found themselves together in Phil's café.

Somewhere around eleven, Declan lowered the last paper and suggested bed.

Kerry gasped.

'For God's sake, Kerry,' he rasped, tossing the paper onto the floor. 'What do you take me for?'

'A man,' said Kerry without thinking.

'And that makes me a monster?'

'No. No, of course it doesn't. But you kissed me, and — '

'A mistake I won't be repeating,' he promised grimly.

'I'm not *that* repulsive,' muttered Kerry.

'No.' He stood up. 'As a matter of fact, you're quite attractive. You are also Kerry Fleming, ex-terror of Carmody

Falls. The young woman I very nearly married — and the last person I'd ever think of compromising.'

'Kissing isn't compromising.' Kerry stared at his taut, angry body, then turned to gaze into the fire. She wished she didn't feel as if he'd kicked her.

'Don't bet on it,' Declan said roughly.

She looked up, puzzled by his sudden harshness. He was holding out his hand.

'Stop sitting there with your mouth open,' he ordered. 'Go find yourself a bed.'

Kerry took the proffered hand gingerly and felt a now familiar thrill run up her arm. Declan looked down as if he, too, had felt something unexpected. His lips tightened, and without speaking he hustled her out into the hall.

'This suit you?' he asked, pausing outside the larger of the two guest bedrooms. 'The sheets are clean. I checked.' He rested a hand on the door above her head.

She nodded, and for one breathless second, as his eyes took on an unusual, opaque cast, Kerry wondered if he would change his mind about kissing her again. But instead he lowered his arm and moved away so abruptly that she blinked.

She waited until he had closed the door of the room across the hall, then followed Barker into her own room. The big dog padded purposefully over to the bed, gave it a good sniff and heaved himself on to the yellow cotton cover.

Kerry pulled him off again and wandered across to the window.

Light from the house was reflected in a shimmering path across the ice. Overhead, a single bright star made all the surrounding stars look like tiny fireflies. A symbol of the season perhaps, thought Kerry wistfully. Of resurrection and rebirth and a man who had long ago risen from the dead.

She drew the curtains together slowly

and, even more slowly, went to pull her nightdress over her head. When she heard the light in Declan's room snap off with a convincing click, she started slightly and tumbled into bed.

Barker sighed noisily and lumbered over to kiss her goodnight.

Kerry turned on her side, ran a hand through the roughness of his fur, and stared blindly into the darkness.

She had wanted Declan to kiss her again out there — wanted it with a hunger that frightened her — wanted so much more than his kiss.

But loving Declan would only lead to heartbreak . . .

Loving? Her fingers stilled on Barker's furry ear. Loving Declan? No. Oh, no. That wasn't possible. She pulled the sheets tightly around her neck. They felt cool and crisp. If only they could protect her from her thoughts . . .

She didn't love Declan. Couldn't love him. It was simple lust that drew her to him as a bee is drawn to the brightness of a flower. Lust. A bodily hunger that

266

happily didn't last. As she, of all people, ought to know. *Did* know. This churning need inside her would soon fade, and the pain that went with it would dull into a peaceful acceptance of her single state. It had to. But for now, all she could do was get through the night, say goodbye to Declan in the morning, and hope that in the clear light of day she would find that she didn't, after all, want his damn body so much it hurt.

She closed her eyes, willing herself to blot Declan out of her mind. Soon he would be back in Toronto playing tiddledywinks with other people's money. And she would be back in Winnipeg running her bookshop.

Kerry waited for some feeling of comfort to follow that thought. But it didn't come. There was no comfort for the hungry demands that racked her body.

She tried rolling on her stomach. It didn't help.

Later, much later, after tossing

restlessly for hours, she finally fell asleep to the drip of melting snow from the eaves, and the gentle sound of canine snoring.

For the first time in months she dreamed of Larry. Except that he had Declan's eyes, and when he kissed her he smelled of soap and spice instead of beer.

The dream faded into heavy, undisturbed sleep.

At five o'clock in the morning Barker demanded to be let out, and she stumbled groggily out of bed to open the door. The garden was fenced. He couldn't go far.

When he hadn't returned by five-fifteen, she went to call him in.

He didn't come.

She tried again at five-thirty, six, and then six-thirty. When he hadn't turned up by seven, Kerry pulled up her collar, tightened the belt on her robe and, taking a deep breath, went to knock on Declan's door.

He opened it wearing white shorts

featuring grinning yellow frogs.

Kerry blinked and managed not to lick her lips. 'Nice,' she said dryly. 'Your Australian girlfriend had imaginative taste. It's too bad I haven't time to admire it.'

A quickly suppressed grin tugged at the corner of Declan's mouth. 'What's your hurry?' he asked, allowing his gaze to rest briefly on the frill of white lace at her throat.

'It's Barker. He's disappeared. I think he must have jumped the fence.' Reluctantly Kerry raised her eyes from the fetching view of yellow frogs covering powerful thighs to concentrate on the business at hand.

'Disappeared? He can't have. There's too damn much of him.'

'All the same, he has. I let him out at five. And he hasn't come back. Can I borrow your car keys? I want to make sure he hasn't wandered up the highway.'

'No,' said Declan, propping himself against the doorframe. 'You can't.'

'But Barker — '

'Barker will be just fine. That hairy mutt knows when he's well off.'

'Maybe, but I have to be sure — '

'I *am* sure,' said Declan.

Kerry glared her distress. 'Declan, will you please stop being a toad and lend me your keys?'

'Not on your life. You, my charming but bubble-headed albatross, are not getting behind the wheel of any car I'm expected to return in one piece.'

'Declan,' said Kerry, not sure whether she wanted to hit him or hug him. 'I've had my driver's license since I was sixteen. If I needed more lessons, I'd take them.'

'You could do with a few,' said Declan, folding his arms. 'And I'm not talking about your driving.'

'You,' said Kerry, 'are the most impossibly supercilious, repellent — '

'Toad,' finished Declan. 'Yes, I know. You've already told me. You're still not driving my car. I have vivid memories of being called out — twice — at three in the morning to extract you and your transportation from roadside vegetation you swore up and down wasn't there.'

Kerry, worried about Barker, unhappy, and frustrated beyond reason by the tantalizing sight of Declan in yellow-frogged shorts, lifted her fists with the intention of smashing them on his temptingly bare chest. But he caught them before they could find their mark.

'You really are asking for trouble, aren't you?' he said softly.

'No,' said Kerry. 'I'm asking for your car keys.'

'Well you're not getting them. That's final, Kerry.'

She took in the cool, black gleam of his eyes, the sensuous curve of his mouth, and longed to take him by the shoulders and shake him. Hard. And force him to acknowledge that she was every bit as capable as he was of conducting herself in a sane and sensible manner behind the wheel. But he wasn't the sort of man who shook easily. And at the moment her wrists

271

were firmly trapped in his hands . . .

Declan smiled suddenly, a curling, incendiary smile that told her he had a very good idea of what was on her mind. And her indignation amused and entertained him.

She bit her lip, and stood quietly in his grip as she weighed her options. His face was only inches above hers and his hair was still damp from the shower. She breathed in, smelled the clean scent of man-in-the-morning — and knew just how she would wipe that complacent smirk off his face. Maybe, in the process, she would also get her hands on his keys . . .

Taking a half step forward, she smiled beguilingly and lifted her lips.

Declan didn't move, didn't react in any way, so she stood on tiptoe and flicked her tongue lightly around the chiseled contours of his mouth.

'Is that what you meant? About trouble?'

'Not exactly.' His voice was about as warm as a cobra's.

When Kerry laughed softly and tossed her hair back, Declan released her wrists and asked pointedly, 'You want me to show you what I meant?'

Kerry eyed him warily. He looked very large, very male, and slightly menacing with those dark, devil's eyebrows slanting upward and that feral little half smile on his lips.

She shook her head. But when he lifted a finger and beckoned, to her horror, she found herself moving toward him.

He waited until she was close enough, then closed his hands purposefully on her hips. She could feel the firm stroke of his palms through her robe.

Kerry's mouth went dry. Her heart started beating much too fast. When Declan shifted his hands to her rear, she gasped.

And in the distance a dog began to bark.

'Barker,' she exclaimed as her heart gradually resumed its normal steady beat. 'Declan, that was Barker.'

'Probably. I told you he'd be all right.' Declan dropped his arms as if he'd discovered he was stroking a jellyfish.

'You don't even care,' Kerry snapped, as angry with herself as she was with him. She should never have let him touch her. And she desperately wanted him to touch her again.

'*Should* I care?' asked Declan, turning his back on her.

The question brought Kerry up short. 'I suppose not,' she admitted. 'But I wish you did.'

He didn't answer, didn't turn around. With a sigh, Kerry left him and went back to her room. She pulled on the first clothes she saw, a red sweater and warm black slacks. Then she shrugged on her parka and hurried outside to find Barker.

The house was surrounded on three sides by trees, but it wasn't hard to pick up the dog's trail. The snow here was deeper, and she could see where

274

something large and bumbling had broken through the patches of icy crust that in some places rose almost to the top of her boots. Thank God, it wasn't midwinter, when she could easily have been buried to her waist.

Kerry pushed her way through a clump of low scrub beneath the trees. A wet branch slapped at her face. She pushed it back and scanned the woods for further signs of Barker's erratic progress.

Suddenly her body went rigid.

She was on the edge of a small clearing from which the snow had all but disappeared. Directly across from her, whimpering softly, lay Barker. He was stretched out on a patch of soggy moss. His right front leg was extended at an odd angle, and as Kerry went closer she saw that it was caught in the jaws of an ugly-looking trap. The trap was attached to the stump of a fallen birch tree.

'Barker,' cried Kerry, running forward, 'Oh, Barker, how could they?'

She knelt down, took the trap in her hands and tried to pry apart the grim-looking jaws. But they were partly rusted and she couldn't get them open. She clenched her teeth, tensed, and tried again.

It was no good. The jaws of the trap remained brutally closed on Barker's paw.

Half sobbing, Kerry bowed her head and clasped her arms around his big, damp neck.

10

'Kerry? Kerry.' Declan's rough voice cut through her moment of despair. She couldn't sit here grieving. Something had to be done about Barker at once.

She lifted a tearstained face to the tall figure stamping through the snow. In the dim light filtering through the frosted branches, he appeared to her as an angel of deliverance. Until he spoke again.

'What the devil do you mean by coming out here alone? You don't know these woods. If there'd been water underneath you could have fallen through and broken your leg.'

Kerry didn't waste time defending herself. Declan was undoubtedly right. Instead she scrambled to her feet and turned to point at Barker.

Declan followed the direction of her finger. His eyes narrowed, and she saw the smooth leather of his gloves tighten around his fists.

'Who in his right mind would set a trap this close to the highway?' he said harshly, looking as if he'd like to get his hands on the trapper's neck. He looked toward the far edge of the clearing where a narrow stream was partially covered by snow. 'Kids, I suppose. Saw water and thought they'd see what they could catch. Barbarous little monsters.'

'Is that legal?' asked Kerry, clamping her lower lip against her teeth.

'Probably not. But that's not likely to weigh much with your average brain-dead adolescent who fancies himself as some kind of macho frontier woods-man.' Moving Kerry peremptorily aside, he knelt down on the damp ground next to Barker. 'It's OK, pal,' he said as desperate brown eyes gazed beseech-ingly upward. 'Don't worry. We'll get you out.' He pushed his sleeves back, reached for the trap, and pulled until every muscle in his forearms was bunched like knotted rope.

The trap sprang apart. Kerry gasped with relief as Barker gave a grateful, whistling sort of sigh and swiped his tongue across his rescuer's nose.

Declan lifted the dog's leg carefully. There were deep pressure marks in his fur, but the flesh didn't seem to be torn. The trap was obviously intended for smaller animals, and although it had stopped Barker in his tracks, nothing was broken. Nor had he attempted to chew himself free, as she knew animals often did in such circumstances. Too bewildered probably.

Kerry heard Declan bite back an oath, and had to clamp her own lips shut to stop herself from expressing her opinion in words she knew would be bound to provoke his censure. She didn't want to provoke Declan at the moment. She was too grateful.

'Is he all right?' she whispered.

'Yes,' he said shortly, after giving the leg a thorough examination. 'You can walk all right, can't you, boy?'

Barker laid his paw gingerly on the wet moss, then bent to lick it. When he was finished he stood up, shook himself, and ambled over to offer the afflicted limb to Kerry.

'Oh, poor Barker,' she murmured, taking it.

Barker promptly removed the paw and, after checking to make sure he had an audience, assumed an exaggerated limp before plodding off in the direction of the house.

'You're not as dumb as you look, are you, my furry friend?' Declan said wryly.

Kerry caught his arm. 'You *do* care about him, don't you?' she exclaimed. 'Oh, Declan . . . ' She gave him a dazzlingly grateful smile.

'What gives you that idea?' He turned away from her to stare at Barker's retreating tail. 'Apart, of course, from the fact that I'd like to strangle those heartless little bastards who set the trap.'

Kerry linked her arm through his and

rubbed her cheek against his sleeve. 'He *will* be all right, won't he?'

'Yes, of course,' Declan said gruffly. 'Don't worry, Kerry. Everything's going to be all right.'

To Kerry it was a voice from her past, brusque, yet infinitely soothing. A voice that had once said, admittedly with a certain edge to it, 'Don't worry, Kerry. You're going to marry *me*.'

With a little cry she turned, flung her arms around him and buried her face in his jacket.

He didn't respond, and when she lifted her head she saw that he was frowning down at her as if she were a burr that had somehow attached itself to his clothing. When his expression changed to a kind of masculine wariness — did he think she was going to burst into tears? — she pulled away and said quickly, 'It's all right, I'm not going to cry.'

'No reason why you should.'

Maybe not, but not everyone could control their emotions the way he did.

'Barker — ' she began.

'Kerry,' Declan said patiently, 'That idiotic dog with the endless supply of pleading paws is the sort who always falls on his feet. Or other people's feet. There is absolutely nothing to cry about.'

'No,' she agreed. 'Of course not.' A fragile tear spilled down her cheek.

Declan brushed it away with the back of his hand and rolled his eyes at the treetops. Then he put a bracing arm around her shoulder and turned her back toward the house.

They ate breakfast without saying much. Declan was busy with the morning paper and Kerry could think of nothing but the parting that lay ahead. A parting that would surely be for good. There wasn't much likelihood that their paths would cross again.

She gazed down at Barker sprawled on his back beside the stove, and it came to her slowly, but with a dawning sense of hopelessness, that she didn't want to say goodbye to Declan. Not today. Not tomorrow. Not ever.

She had made a terrible mistake seven years ago. And there was nothing she could do to erase it.

Kerry swallowed and gazed hopelessly at the top of Declan's head. It was all she could see of him above the paper. When he sensed her attention, he looked up. She stumbled quickly to her feet.

'I — I have to pack,' she explained.

She'd already packed. But she had to leave him, had to be by herself. If she stayed she would give herself away.

As Declan returned to his paper, Barker licked his lips and heaved himself up to plod after her.

The aroma of coffee followed them down the hall.

Feeling a bit like a tire with a slow leak, Kerry slumped onto a floral-printed chair by her bedroom window. She stared at the freshly made bed. But her mind wasn't on the handsome, irresponsible man with whom she had once shared another, much larger bed.

It was on the man she had left sitting in Harry's kitchen.

Dear God, what a fool she had been. Kerry wiped a hand across her eys.

But she couldn't wipe out the memories.

Memories of Declan, the tyrant in tight jeans, bending over to kiss her goodnight. Of Declan, the toast of Carmody Falls, dancing with a raw eroticism that had stirred her blood as no man had stirred it before. And of Declan, the man she had always trusted, kissing her in extravagant revenge.

No. Kerry forced her thoughts away from that disturbingly improbable memory. But almost at once, like the shifting scenes of a dream, another image took its place — of Declan's face when he had seen Barker in the trap. In a way, she was glad the trap's owners hadn't been around to receive the rough justice he had looked ready to mete out. Yet how gently he had dealt with Barker, the dog he hadn't even wanted around . . .

That was when the truth finally hit her. It was like a bright light exploding in her head.

Declan was not, and probably never had been, the repressive, sensible autocrat she had once been so certain she knew.

Yes, he was sensible enough most of the time, and certainly autocratic. But he was kind as well as domineering, and when, in the past, he had appeared arrogant and dictatorial, it had usually been for good reason.

Was it possible, then, that her long-standing resentment of his authority had always been more than a natural striving for independence?

Kerry groaned, as the pieces of the enigma fell mercilessly into place. It wasn't Declan's authority she had resented. It was the power he held over her emotions. By some devious magic only dimly detected until this moment, he had maneuvered his way into her heart and taken it over as easily as he took over new stock issues.

And she had let him. Because she loved him.

Kerry drew a harsh, shuddering breath and covered her face with both hands.

She wasn't sure how long she sat there frozen with shock and a new and painful self-awareness, before she felt Barker's nose nudge her knee.

Automatically she put out a hand to pat him — and the movement stirred her senses back to life.

What was she doing sitting here like a wilted rosebud behaving as if her world had just caved in? She couldn't allow it to cave in. She had a bookshop to run, a life to get on with. It wasn't all over. Just because she had managed to fall in love with the man she had turned her back on seven years ago, was no reason to turn her back on the future.

Kerry squared her shoulders. 'There's no excuse for giving up without a fight,' she announced bravely to Barker.

Barker offered her a paw.

'I know,' she said, taking it. 'I had my chance, didn't I? And Declan isn't, in a million years, likely to give me another. Unless I can somehow prove to him that I'm no longer flighty, air-headed Kerry who can't even be trusted to say, 'I do,' when she's supposed to.'

Barker, sensing her distraction, jumped up to lie beside her on the bed. As soon as she turned toward him, he closed his eyes.

'Off,' said Kerry wearily. 'You're not invisible just because you can't see me any longer.'

Barker sighed, scratched his ear, and tumbled reproachfully to the floor. After a while, the warmth left by his body began to steal its way into Kerry's limbs. When it settled deep in her belly and set fiery needles pricking at her nerve ends, it finally came to her what she had to do.

'It might work,' she murmured to Barker. 'Might even lead to something more. After all, Declan is a man.'

Barker grunted, and Kerry smiled

wistfully. 'You're right,' she said. 'The trouble with Declan is that he suffers from a tiresome disease called integrity. But it's not as if I'm some kind of sacred trust. I mean, I *have* been married. It wouldn't be as if he were taking something that couldn't be replaced.'

Except her heart. But he couldn't know he had that already. Unless she told him.

She sighed, and Barker put his head between his paws and blinked at her.

'I know,' said Kerry. 'Life's tough. But so am I. I've had to be.' She pressed her knuckles against her eyelids and ignored the sudden tightness in her chest as for one short, blissful moment the fire in her belly subsided, and she allowed herself to imagine spending a whole lifetime with Declan. It wouldn't be any bed of roses. More like thistles. But even so . . .

Stop it, Kerry. She halted herself in mid-fantasy. Time enough to think of the future when she'd settled a more immediate need.

She tugged off her red V-neck sweater and, gazing glumly at her plain cotton camisole, decided it would just have to do. Then, with her heart thundering in her ears, she padded along the passage to the kitchen.

There was no one there.

Her bloodstream began to cool down.

She hesitated. Declan must have gone to his room.

'What the *hell* do you think you're doing?' demanded a bitingly irate voice from behind her.

Kerry jumped as if she'd been punctured with a pin.

'Declan!' she gasped. 'Why — what . . .'

'That's what I'd like to know,' Declan snapped. 'What do you think you're doing parading around half naked in Harry's kitchen?'

She gaped at him. He had changed from casual clothes back into a shirt and trousers, ready for the flight back to Toronto. Already he seemed distant,

289

less approachable.

'I'm not half naked.' Kerry was aware that her reply lacked conviction, but his anger had taken her by surprise. After all, he'd seen her in less back at the Cambrian. And hadn't seemed particularly fazed.

He flipped a finger at the strap of her camisole. 'What do you call this, then? Street attire? Or are you posing as a donation from some sleazy escort service?'

'Oh! Oh, how could you?' Kerry raised her hand. But after taking one look at his face, she changed her mind. The tanned skin covering his cheekbones was pulled taut. The light in his eyes was scorching in its intensity, and she thought she had never seen his crooked mouth so hard. It was as if, suddenly, all the years of friendship and exasperated affection counted for nothing — as if he were looking at a stranger. A stranger he wanted to hurt. But — Declan had never hurt her. Not really . . .

Slowly Kerry let her hand drop back to her side. The bright kitchen all at once seemed dreary, the smell of coffee old and stale. But as she gazed at him, confused and hurting, the look in his eyes pierced her momentary paralysis, and she remembered the reason she was here.

'Not sleazy,' she said, batting her eyelashes at him in a way that would have won Maybelle's admiration. She rotated her hips in a taunting parody of seduction, knowing it would provoke the opposite reaction to the one she dreamed of, but wanting in some way to pay him back. 'I only provide quality service.' She moved her hips some more.

'Kerry! For God's sake . . . ' Declan started to reach for her, then drew a harsh breath and abruptly turned his back. 'I didn't see that,' he said.

Kerry felt an acid glow of triumph. She had got through to him. But triumph faded as she began to realize how small a victory she had won.

'Didn't you?' she said, with a bitterness she made no attempt to hide. 'Then maybe I should do it again.'

'What?' Declan swung around, his hard gaze settling on the quick rise and fall of her breasts which the thin camisole did little to conceal. Then, as Kerry watched him, waiting for his next move, he squared his jaw and unfastened the top button of his shirt.

'No,' he said, his voice still unresponsively harsh. 'I wouldn't like you to repeat that outrageous exhibition, thank you. I'd like you to get dressed.'

She moistened her lips. It was now or never. She hadn't been able to slip quietly into the kitchen as she had planned, to put her arms around him and kiss those harshly defined lips until they softened. But he had called her half naked. And deep down she knew he wasn't indifferent to her nakedness. Had not been indifferent for some time.

Maybe, after all, there was hope.

But he wasn't going to make this easy. She should have known he wouldn't. Declan rarely made anything easy.

'Are you saying you don't find me attractive?' she asked, looking him straight in the eye.

'No. I find you attractive. Who wouldn't?' Still that hard, grating tone.

'Then why — oh, for heaven's sake.' He was standing there looking so coldly distant, so unbending — and so damn sexy — that she found herself losing her temper along with her head. 'Can't you help me out?'

'Help you out? You'll have to explain yourself, Kerry.'

'Don't pretend you don't understand me.' She was almost shouting now, from humiliation as well as from frustration. 'You know very well what I mean. I want to go to bed with you, dammit . . . ' She broke off appalled by the impassiveness with which Declan was greeting her admission.

'If I didn't know it before, I do now,' he said austerely.

Kerry made a stupendous effort to

get her emotions under control. 'Declan,' she said, forcing herself to meet his blue-black stare. 'I know you want me. I used to think you didn't, but I was wrong. Wasn't I? And I don't see any sense in playing games. Do you?' She pushed both hands through her hair. 'I understand that you won't want to marry me. Why should you after what happened last time? But I'm a big girl now. I make my own decisions. So I'd like — I'd like to make love with you. At least once.' She twisted her lips into a semblance of a smile. 'Don't look at me as if you think I've lost my mind. I promise you I know what I'm doing.'

'Do you?' Declan didn't look at her. Instead he concentrated on unfastening a cuff. 'That's debatable.'

'Declan . . . ' Without knowing quite what she meant to do, Kerry took a step toward him.

Immediately he stepped back and started unfastening the other cuff. Then he rolled up his sleeves.

Kerry ran her tongue around her lips. 'Declan,' she said, 'What are you doing?'

He looked up at last, but she couldn't tell a thing from the carved immobility of his features. He looked as though he was getting ready for some hard manual labor. Her stomach gave an uncontrollable lurch.

All right then. If Declan insisted on playing games, she would call his bluff.

Lifting her chin, she inhaled deeply and moved swiftly to close the space between them. Then, leaving him no time to guess what she was up to, she unfastened the remaining buttons on his shirt.

He didn't move. Instead he stood staring down at her with the muscles of his jaw pulled so tight she could see the veins standing out in his neck. Only when she began to unbuckle his belt did he choose to act.

Kerry heard the belt fall to the floor just before he lifted her off her feet.

She gave a little cry as he strode with

her through the door and across the hall, and another when he dropped her onto the bed in his room. It was huge, and it had a black satin quilt. She noted that with a sense of unreality, feeling the smoothness of the satin against her legs.

Declan sat now, removed his shoes, and stretched himself out beside her. After that she was conscious of nothing but his body and the scent of desire.

'OK. Satisfied?' he asked harshly.

She could feel the length of him all along her side, feel the hardness of his hip pressing into her and the warmth of his thigh against her leg. 'No,' she gasped, pushing herself up on one elbow. She gazed down at the hard expanse of his chest so deliciously set off by the white folds of his unbuttoned shirt. 'No. And neither are you.'

It was true. Lying this close to him, she would have had to be blind and without a sense of touch not to notice that he was as much aroused as she was. 'I said I don't see any sense playing games,' she whispered when he made no response.

He raised a hand, placed it over her breast. 'Don't you?' he said, revolving his thumb in a slow, erotic motion over the flimsy white cotton barrier.

'No. No, I don't,' Kerry whispered. 'I want you, Declan. As much as I think you want me.'

She watched his chest expand as he drew more air into his lungs. 'Maybe I do.'

'Then — '

He withdrew the hand, turned on his back and fixed his gaze on the ceiling.

Kerry felt black satin pull tight across her stomach. Watching Declan, holding her breath, Kerry saw that he looked gaunt, hollow-eyed, as though he hadn't slept for days.

'Kerry,' he said after a silence that seemed to last forever. 'Kerry, I'm sorry. I lost my temper. But I am not, repeat not, about to take advantage of a charmingly enticing young woman who appears to have the survival instincts of a suicidal moth.' The rough edge to his voice told Kerry that his body was as tortured as hers was.

'You wouldn't be taking advantage,' she said softly, trailing a finger from the pulsing hollow of his neck down to the waistband of his trousers.

Declan groaned. 'Kerry, for God's sake . . . ' He moved over her suddenly and pressed his hands into the covers beside her head.

In her numbed imagination, he appeared balanced above her like some great dark bird of prey. She looked into his eyes, sulphurous midnight pools reflecting anger, frustration, desire — torment even — but no trace of tenderness. Nor was there any tenderness in his voice when he spoke again.

'Get out,' he said wearily. 'Get out now, Kerry, before I do something we'll both regret.'

'Don't tell me you have a headache?' Kerry tried to smile, to wall over the aching emptiness in her heart, but her lips wouldn't do what she told them.

'You could put it that way. A headache called Kerry Fleming.'

He was speaking, almost, in the old, teasing tone she remembered from her childhood. But she sensed the effort it cost him. 'Declan,' she whispered, curving her hand over his freshly shaven cheek. 'Declan, I promise you I won't regret — '

'Dammit, Kerry, I said get out.' He wasn't teasing now, he was roaring, and he pushed her hand away and rolled off the bed so fast she scarcely saw him move. Then he was standing, and his hands were on her shoulders hauling her upward.

Kerry fixed her eyes on her feet, waiting for Declan to let her go. When he didn't, she looked up.

He was standing with head lowered and his dark hair falling across his face — like some old-time brigand bent on plunder, she thought wildly. And even though he had refused to plunder, Kerry knew that for once Declan was not the disciplined, imperturbable man she had loved, in one form or another, for the better part of her life. He was someone else altogether. Someone who had the power to hurt her as she had never known hurt before.

The time for evasions was over. If the truth trampled her pride into the dust, what did it matter? Somehow she had to make Declan give her a chance to prove she was a woman — a woman who could make her own decisions with her eyes wide open and without falling apart or running to him for help.

'I love you,' she said, placing her palms over the hard hands gripping her shoulders. 'Don't send me away.'

Declan growled something she didn't catch. But before she could ask what he'd said, he was behind her and pointing her at the door.

'I have to send you away.' His voice was so harsh it made her wince. 'You don't love me, Kerry. What you feel is purely infatuation. A certain affection combined with a healthy dose of lust. I'm sorry I can't give you what you want, but I simply haven't the time to play nursemaid anymore.'

Kerry tried to turn around, but he wouldn't let her.

'No,' he said. 'I know what you're going to say. That you've changed, that you're a mature and capable business-woman these days. And maybe you have changed. But you're still Kerry, and I'm not the marrying kind.'

'You were once,' said Kerry, hearing the break in her voice, hating it, and hating that he could hear it, too. 'I wasn't asking you to marry me.'

'I couldn't offer you less than marriage, Kerry.'

Was there a certain rough tenderness in his tone? It was hard to tell, because if tenderness existed, he was deter-mined not to let it show.

'I expect you're right,' she said, salvaging what remained of her pride. 'We wouldn't suit each other.'

'We'd be a full-scale disaster,' Declan muttered. He shoved her out into the hall. 'Hurry up and get dressed, or both of us are going to miss our flights.'

Kerry stumbled across the floor and into her room. Barker's tail thumped a drowsy welcome as she closed the door and slumped against the wall.

Dismissed. As if she were still the little girl he was used to ordering around. But for a moment there, when he had lain beside her on the bed, he hadn't looked on her as a little girl. She had *seen* the desire in his eyes. And elsewhere.

Kerry gazed drearily out of the window at the bare winter branches of the birch trees. How *could* Declan have done that to her? How could the man she had loved and hated and trusted all her life have taken her into his bed in some kind of reprisal, then thrown her out as if he'd done it by mistake? Or as if it was the honorable thing to do. Declan always did the honorable thing . . .

If only, for once, he could have acted on instinct instead of principle, she might at least have had a morning to remember.

Kerry trailed over to the dresser and sat down. Emptiness. Life without Declan, who had become the beat and the rhythm of her heart. That was what she had to look forward to. There was no sense deluding herself. Declan's honor would never let him take advantage of Kerry Fleming. He did want her, hadn't even tried to deny it. But he didn't love her, didn't believe in love except as lust. And because she was who she was, he wouldn't take from her what he knew he couldn't return.

She supposed she ought to admire him for his principles. She didn't though. She resented him, hated his principles. And, dammit, he'd had no need to humiliate her, to make her feel like some cheap little tart . . .

She buried her face in her hands. They smelled of Barker as well as of Declan. Dear lord, how, after that scene in his bedroom, could she possibly face Declan again?

Sometime later Kerry lifted her head,

saw her white, strained face in the mirror, and had her answer.

If she made herself scarce until his flight left, she wouldn't *have* to see him again. There would be no need to face him. Ever. No need to endure the pain of that final, agonizing goodbye.

He'd be angry, of course, when he found her gone. But he'd get over it, be relieved in a way. And she would be safely out of his orbit before he had a chance to twist the knife any deeper.

Kerry gripped the edge of the dresser and bowed her head.

Barker, sensing her grief, rubbed his head along her leg and sat down companionably on her feet. Kerry bent to pat him — and knew that if she meant to act she would have to do it now, at once, before her courage failed her.

'Don't worry, I'll be back,' she whispered to Barker. 'Just hang on for a couple of hours.'

Barker wagged his tail, and Kerry fought off her lethargy and forced herself to stand up. Hurriedly she pulled her sweater back on. Then she scrabbled in her purse for a pen and located a torn scrap of paper.

'Declan,' she wrote. '*Thank you for the ride. I've gone for a walk. By the time I come back you'll be gone, so could you leave the key in the same place. I won't forget to put it back. Please leave Barker in the kitchen.*' She hesitated, and then wrote, '*Love, Kerry.*'

It was done. Now all she had to do was prop the note against the mirror, pull on her jacket and boots — and get out.

Barker looked up reproachfully as she left, but he made no sound as she moved quietly through the hall to the front door. A second later she was outside, running and stumbling along the snow-rutted road to the highway.

She didn't realize she was crying until she felt the icy touch of tears on her cheeks.

11

Kerry fidgeted uncomfortably on a stool in front of the bar of the King's Moose. A numbing sense of loss, of mindless indifference to her surroundings, had kept her from caring about anything at first. But gradually, as the pain began to come back, she became aware that the bartender was staring down the front of her sweater.

Her face began to turn red. She might have lost the man who had filled every corner of her mind from the moment he had come back into her life, but that didn't mean she had lost all self-respect. Nor did she have to sit here like a blank-faced mannequin enduring the lecherous attentions of any sweaty, overweight bartender.

She pulled herself up straight and tried to look the man squarely in the eye. But the eye was riveted on her cleavage and he didn't notice. Kerry shifted on her stool and leaned backward. The bartender leaned forward. Kerry leaned further back.

'Look . . . ' she began.

Her sentence was never completed. As she swiveled sideways, determined to cut off the man's view, she lost her balance and began to slide off the stool. She made a wild grab for the bar. Just a second too late.

With a bruising thump, she landed flat on her back on the tiled floor.

'Hell of a crash-landing,' remarked a cheerful male voice from above her.

Kerry gulped, and looked warily upward. A thin man in a cowboy hat was grinning down at her and holding out his hand. He had a friendly smile and looked reassuringly safe. Kerry took the hand, and he pulled her to her feet.

'OK?' he asked, patting her shoulder as she leaned against him trying to catch her breath.

'I'm fine,' Kerry gasped. 'More or

less.' She laughed hollowly. 'I'm so sorry. Clumsy of me.'

'Not to worry.' He slipped an encouraging arm around her waist. 'Here, let me find us a table — '

'I'll take care of that,' said an iron-hard voice from the entrance. 'Kerry, come here.'

Oh, God. Kerry closed her eyes, as the cowboy's arm slid from her waist. Declan *hadn't* taken her note at face value. She must have been out of her mind to think he would. When Declan took on a job he always saw it through to the bitter end. And if the tone of his voice was anything to go by, to him that was precisely what she was. A bitter end he could have done without.

But she had never wanted to be a burden. She had wanted to be left alone to find her own kind of peace — as one day she would, when the pain of losing him had dulled.

There could be no question of peace for the next hour. Not when Declan was being his old, tyrannical self.

Kerry stared at a loose button on the cowboy's shirt. 'I'm not a dog, Declan,' she said, forcing herself to speak calmly. 'I don't come to heel on command.'

When he didn't answer at once she raised her eyes.

He was draped in the doorway with his hands in the pockets of his trousers. In his dark, expensive coat, and with his skin still glowing from the cold, he looked intense, compelling, hypnotically attractive and blazing angry.

Kerry took a half step toward him and stopped.

'Declan?' She swallowed, holding out her hand in a gesture that was both defiance and supplication.

Why was he looking at her like that? As if she'd committed some unmentionable atrocity?

'I said, come here,' he repeated, ignoring the hand.

'Declan, what's the matter with you? You've no right . . . ' She paused. No, he had no right, no reasonable claim on her. If he had, she might have put up with his Victorian father act — if only for the sake of harmony . . .

'You were saying?' said Declan, in a tone that reminded her of a steel blade ripping through silk.

Kerry ran her tongue over her teeth. 'I'm not going with you, Declan. You'd better leave now or you'll miss your plane.'

'I've already missed it.' He ran a brisk eye over a row of coats in the corner and went to sweep Kerry's off its hanger. 'Put this on.' He handed it to her. 'Since less civilized options aren't open to me, I'm taking you back to the house.'

'Declan, I don't want or need — '

'No. But, as I said, what you do need I'm not at liberty to apply.'

Kerry gave a brittle, unconvincing laugh. 'What a violent man you are,' she scoffed. 'You must find the laws of the land a great trial to you.'

'No, Ms. Fleming, I do not. I find you a great trial to me. Now, do I — ?'

Kerry shrugged resignedly. 'No, you

don't have to carry me,' she said.

She had always known when to give in to Declan, so she knew better than most that there was no point in arguing with him when he was in one of his Victorian moods. There would, after all, be no avoiding that final goodbye. She had no option now but to survive the next hour or two and hope to heaven there was another flight leaving for Toronto very soon.

As Declan helped her on with her coat, she stole a surreptitious glance at his face. His eyes were hard, as inscrutable as she had ever seen them. And yet she had a feeling the mask that formed his features was concealing something — some emotion, perhaps, that he didn't want her to see? Or wasn't willing to acknowledge . . . ?

'Come on.' He took her arm and urged her towards the entrance.

Kerry hung back. 'Thanks for picking me up,' she said to the man in the cowboy hat, who was watching them from under its brim.

'Any time,' he grunted. 'Sure you're all right, miss?'

'I — ' She darted another glance at Declan, who was beginning to remind her of a glacier that was just about to crack. No, she wasn't sure of anything. All the same, she said, 'Yes, thank you, I'm fine,' and with her lips firmly pressed together allowed Declan to lead her from the room.

When she looked at him again, his mouth had flattened to the point where his lips had all but disappeared.

Kerry shut her eyes. This was unbearable. Worse than any physical pain. She balled her free hand into a fist. Why, oh, why, when she had finally come to realize she loved Declan, had he turned back into the controlling, overbearing dictator she no longer truly believed he was?

She studied his profile, seeking an answer that wasn't there. It was bleak, unrelenting, in keeping with the merciless pace at which he was marching her through the snow. Then suddenly she found she couldn't breathe. Because for half a split second, when he turned to look at her, she saw beneath the frozen surface to the flaming passion he was struggling to suppress.

'Declan?' she said uncertainly. 'Declan, what is it? What's the matter?'

'You are,' he said, so grimly that she blanched.

Kerry knew better than to ask what he meant. She was familiar with that end-of-conversation tone. But the look in his eyes, their surprising passion . . . ? She stared at the tire marks in the snow, willing herself not to hope.

Ten minutes later they were back at the house and Barker was greeting them joyfully at the door.

Declan unzipped Kerry's jacket, hustled her into the kitchen and sat her down. Then he tossed his own coat over a chair and, standing across from her, pressed his fists on the table and leaned toward her. As if I'm a prisoner in the dock and he's counsel for the prosecution, thought Kerry, half hysterically.

313

'Why, Kerry?' he demanded.

She dropped her eyes. 'Why what?'

'You know very well why what. First, why did you run out on me? Second, what the devil do you mean by making a spectacle of yourself in the King's Moose?'

Kerry shook her head. It didn't quite seem to belong to her. 'I wasn't making a spectacle of myself. I fell off my stool because I was trying to avoid the bartender's eyes. He was leering down the front of my sweater.'

Declan's mouth turned down. 'I'm not surprised.'

'What's that supposed to mean?' Kerry got up and went to pour herself a glass of water.

'That if you will go around dressed like a scarlet invitation to bed and breakfast, you can't expect not to be taken up on it.'

Her strange light-headedness grew worse. She ought to feel angry. Was angry. But she was also flattered in a sense. *And* just plain hurt. She drained

314

her glass of water in one breath. 'Would you take me up on it?' she asked.

No answer, and she was forced to turn around.

Declan looked grimly astonished, as if she had asked him how he'd like to take his clothes off so they could get down to business on the table. Which, come to think of it, was an idea that had a certain raw appeal. She filled her glass again, trailed back to the chair and sat down. Barker sighed.

Declan's knuckles turned white against the wood. 'No,' he said coldly. 'I wouldn't. I don't pick up stray bedmates in bars.'

Kerry gripped her hands in her lap. 'Neither do I,' she said.

'No? Then I apologize.' Muscles worked in his throat and he added with an apparent effort to maintain his temper, 'You haven't answered the first part of my question.'

Kerry ran her finger along the smooth, cool edge of the table. Why had she set herself up for rejection? She had known what his answer would be. But when she said nothing, and went on staring at the table, Declan leaned across it to grasp her wrist.

His touch blasted such a wave of heat through her bloodstream that she would have fallen if she hadn't been sitting down. She took a quick mouthful of ice-cold water and whispered, 'Don't touch me.'

Declan dropped her wrist as if he'd accidentally picked up a hot coal.

'Are you going to answer me?' he demanded.

Curiously, and in spite of, or perhaps because of, her profound unhappiness, Declan's peremptory words, and his assumption that he had a right to demand answers, roused in her the will to fight back.

'You know why I left,' she said. 'I couldn't face the thought of saying goodbye to you after — ' She broke off as Declan lowered himself into a chair. He was looking at her as if he thought she'd lost her mind. 'After what happened,' she finished, issuing a challenge with her eyes.

'What are you talking about? Nothing happened. And you must have known that having brought you and that lamentable mutt this far, I'd at least make sure the two of you got home. Assuming I didn't murder you first,' he added grimly.

'Why should you do that?' She lifted her chin, daring him to touch her.

Declan leaned back in his chair and glared at the tap which she hadn't quite turned off. 'Because I've sometimes felt it was either that or make love to you on the spot.'

Kerry gasped and lowered her chin at once. Did he mean it? He certainly didn't look loverlike. And he had spoken in his business-shark voice. Murder seemed the likelier option.

'Charming,' she murmured, with only a very slight crack in her voice. 'I didn't know you went in for that sort of sex.'

'I don't.' Declan rested his forearms on the table and bent toward her. There was a controlled ferocity about him now that made Kerry cast a wary glance at the door. 'I can accept your aversion to goodbyes,' he said. 'But shall we try to behave like adults? I'll drive you to the airport and you can make your own arrangements from there. I won't attempt to say goodbye.'

Kerry nodded. He was right, of course. The sooner they made arrangements to return to their respective homes, the sooner this agonizing farce would be over. She should never have run from Declan in the first place. And if it was revenge he had wanted for past betrayals, he had certainly got it. She felt wrung out, empty, blinded by the knowledge that she had lost him.

She started to get up, and Barker put his head on her lap.

Funny, lovable Barker. She still had him.

Bending down so Declan wouldn't see her tears, Kerry threw her arms around the big dog's sympathetic neck. She buried her face in his rough fur.

Even if it choked her, she wasn't going to let Declan know how desperately she was hurting. Let him think of her as a female Peter Pan who would never grow up, never be seriously wounded by his rejection. At least *his* heart would be at peace.

When she finally stood up, Barker, ever alert to the possibility of food, stood with her and moved between her legs. She stumbled and grabbed for the back of the nearest chair. But Declan was there first, and before she could reach it he had caught her in his arms.

Kerry gazed up at him, stunned. The sun shining through the window had cast deep shadows across his hawklike features. Heavy lines were etched across his forehead. Yet there was a light in his eyes that seemed to radiate from within, a light so intense she felt as if her skin had been scorched.

His embrace was strong, masterful. She didn't mind the heat. If only they could remain like this forever . . .

Holding her breath, Kerry reached up, touched a tentative finger to his lips. 'Declan . . . ?' she whispered.

'Kerry.' He smoothed his hand down the length of her hair. 'Kerry, don't look at me like that.'

His voice was husky, as if he had something lodged in his throat. Kerry tried to smile, but it was a wavering, unsuccessful smile that made Declan shake his head and say, 'When you look like that, all bruised and brave and sad, you make me want to pound my head against a wall.'

'Don't,' said Kerry, lowering her eyes so he wouldn't see the desolation she couldn't hide. 'Declan, please . . . '

'I'm sorry.' He patted her on the back as if he didn't know what else to do. But when she made to pull away, he put a hand under her chin and tipped her face up. 'You seem so fragile all of a sudden.' He shook his head. 'Like a lily whose petals have been crushed.'

Had he really said that? Had Declan, who had many times accused her of being a delinquent, actually called her a lily? Kerry was still gaping at him when he bent his head to kiss her.

It started as a gentle kiss, warm, soft, tinglingly delicious. But within seconds the gentleness had given way to a rough, hungry plundering that left her gasping for breath and desperate to escape. When she tasted the sharp tang of mint on his tongue, she knew she had to get away at once, now, before the damage he was doing to her heart became irreversible.

Twisting herself out of his grasp, she pushed him away and ran, half sobbing, for the safety of her room.

When she heard Declan pounding after her, she slammed the door in his face.

'Kerry!' he shouted from the hallway. 'Kerry, open up this minute.'

She ignored him, and a moment later the wall shuddered under the impact of his fist.

Kerry didn't jump. She wasn't capable of jumping. She was only capable of collapsing against the paneling to stare, glazed with indecision, at the melted snow dripping from the eaves.

But she hadn't locked the door. When she didn't answer, Declan yanked it open, letting in a blast of warm air.

Kerry looked at him and started to shiver.

'Kerry,' he said, through barely parted teeth. 'Kerry, so help me . . .'

She couldn't see him properly because there seemed to be a thick fog in front of her eyes. But she could hear him. He was breathing heavily and striding back and forth across the room. After a while his steps slowed, came to a stop, and she felt strong hands lock around her wrists.

She flinched away, startled.

'It's all right, Kerry.' Declan was still angry, but she could tell his anger was under control. 'There's no need to stand there quivering like a frightened kitten. I'm not going to hurt you. For all I probably should.'

Kerry closed her eyes. Was she dreaming that note of exasperated tenderness in his voice? Dreaming that he had drawn her against him, lifted her arms and placed them around his neck? She could feel the safe, solid hardness of his body through his silk shirt, smell the masculine cleanliness of his skin, hear the roughness in his voice as he murmured, 'Kerry. Kerry, sweetheart. For God's sake don't cry. I've got a better idea. Kiss me instead.'

She only resisted for a moment. Then his nearness, and the magnetism that had drawn her to him long before she understood its meaning, made her respond to him in spite of all her doubts — in spite of the knowledge that she was giving him back the chance to break her heart.

Briefly, she stood still, drawing the scent of him into her nostrils, safe in the sanctuary of his arms . . .

When he began to move his hands slowly across her back, and she felt his fingers wind themselves in her hair, she pressed her body to his and kissed him very softly on the mouth.

'Declan?' she murmured. 'Oh, Declan . . . ?'

'Yes,' he said. 'It's me. The toad. Why did you run away again, Kerry?'

Kerry tumbled back to earth with a bump. 'You mean just now?' she asked cautiously.

'That'll do for a start.'

'I don't know. I was scared.'

'Of me?'

'No. Yes. I mean I was scared you'd hurt me . . . '

She heard the quick rasp of his breath. 'Kerry, what do you take me for? Don't you know I'd never — '

'No. No, wait.' She placed a finger over his lips. 'Not that kind of hurt. That might be easier to bear. I meant I was afraid . . . ' She stopped. She was still afraid. Afraid that Declan couldn't love her. Because she was Kerry. 'I'm sorry. I don't know what I meant,' she said quickly. 'I think I must have been dreaming.'

Declan put his hands on her shoulders and backed her up against the wall. 'You can dream all you like, Kerry Fleming. Provided you dream about me. Got that?'

Kerry's heart did an unexpected back-flip. Was she still dreaming? Or was this really Declan, the hard-headed man who believed love was for ingenuous romantics?

'I thought — ' she began cautiously.

'Don't. Kerry, sweetheart, you were always much better at acting than thinking. Don't spoil it now.'

Kerry stopped melting and opened her mouth to tell him just what she thought of rude, patronizing toads who hadn't yet turned into handsome princes. But she only got as far as 'toad' before he silenced her firmly with a kiss.

It was a hungry, possessive kiss, the kiss of a man determined to stake a claim. But soon it softened, became gentler, kinder, a kiss that spoke of love and forever. A kiss between two people who were complete in themselves but who together could build rainbows and touch the moon. Kerry wanted it to go on till morning.

Eagerly she ran her fingers over Declan's face and down his neck, absorbing the feel of him, reveling in the tough, smooth tautness of his skin. But gradually, as their embrace deepened, she began to be aware that not even Declan's warmth could make her feel as if her legs were wrapped in wool, nor was his closeness likely to make her foot go numb.

It was, after all, too cold for rainbows. Her fingers couldn't reach as far as the moon. And Barker was sitting on her foot.

Kerry landed squarely back on earth when Declan pushed Barker gently away and, holding her at arm's length, said sternly, 'Kerry, it's taken me half a lifetime to figure out that you're my Queen of Hearts. And I'm damned if I mean to share your feet with a dog.'

'Is that all you care about?' she asked.

'What? Your feet? No, there are one or two other parts of you to which I hope to give my undivided attention fairly soon.' He gave her a meaningful little pat on the backside.

'Declan?' Kerry gazed up at him in doubt, apprehension and hope. 'Does that mean — '

'It means,' said Declan, with a crooked smile, 'that you and I have some talking to do. And that we are *not* going to do it in your bedroom. Because if we did, something tells me talking wouldn't happen.'

Kerry's heart sank. Was he saying all he wanted to do was *talk*? Surely after the kiss they had just shared . . .

She never did get around to finishing the thought, because Declan suddenly turned businesslike, and before she knew what he was up to, he had scooped her up in his arms, marched into the bright, oak-paneled living room and sat down with her in a comfortable tweed chair.

'Now,' he said, settling her firmly on

his knee. 'You were saying?'

'I wasn't.' She gulped, feeling the firmness of his thighs through her slacks as every nerve in her body came alert. 'At least — Declan, I don't understand. I thought you didn't want — I mean —'

'Didn't want what, Kerry?'

'Me,' she said in a small voice.

Declan groaned and shut his eyes. But after a while he dropped his hand to her knee and admitted quietly, 'So did I in the beginning. It never once occurred to me when you turned up in Carmody Falls that there was a damn good reason I refused to let you out of my sight.' He paused, as if he were having trouble finding words. 'It seemed to me you were still doing crazy things — and protecting you from yourself was what I'd always done. It wasn't easy to admit my feelings for you had changed. That I was beginning to wonder if I'd made the mistake of a lifetime when I allowed you to turn me in for a younger model.'

Was that a break she heard in his voice? Kerry looked up, her heart filling with hope and dismay in equal measures. 'Declan, you're not — are you — saying you've always cared for me. Since I was a girl?' She waited, not daring to believe.

'No,' said Declan.

Kerry knew her face must have shown her consternation, because at once he touched a finger to her nose and said gravely, 'You know I've always *cared* for you, Kerry. No man in his right mind would have put up with you for as long as I have if he hadn't cared.'

He was fond of her. That was all. Kerry dropped her eyes, finding she didn't have the spirit or the heart to insist yet again that she was no longer the immature child whose antics he had so long deplored and endured.

'I suppose that's true,' she said drearily. 'Larry didn't put up with me.'

Declan frowned and pulled her head against his shoulder. 'But, as we've already established, Larry *didn't* give a damn. Which is why there are times when I wish your decently deceased husband was still around.'

'I don't,' said Kerry, not caring that he wasn't making sense. Not caring about anything much.

'No, I don't suppose you do.' There was an improbable hint of laughter in Declan's voice. 'But then I doubt if you've ever suffered from any particular urge to rearrange his nose.' He bent his head to drop a kiss in the vee of her red sweater.

Kerry gasped, torn between laughter and tears. 'No. No, I suppose I haven't,' she agreed.

'Good. And don't go getting any ideas about my nose. I won't put up with it.' Declan ran his palm smoothly down her spine.

Kerry sat up and perched on the very edge of his knee. She couldn't stand this any longer. Was Declan saying what she wanted him to say? Or was she fooling herself, dreaming the dreams of an incurable optimist held captive by his tantalizing closeness?

'Declan,' she said, making herself look him in the eye. 'What are you trying to tell me?'

He put his hands on her hips and shifted her up against him.

'Kerry — sweetheart — I'm trying to say I'm sorry. Sorry I hurt you. I won't pretend I didn't know what I was doing. I did. At the time it seemed the only thing to do. If I'd been kind, treated you gently, I thought it would make it that much harder for you to get over your . . . ' He hesitated, frowning.

'Infatuation,' finished Kerry bleakly. Had she been offered the moon only to have it snatched from beneath her nose?

'Yes,' said Declan, making no attempt to soften the truth. 'But now I believe — hope — it may be more than that.' He took her face in his hands and tipped it upward, and she saw the doubt, the longing, the passionate hunger in his eyes.

'Oh, yes, it's more,' she whispered. 'Much, much more.'

Beneath her, his body relaxed. Tenderly he smoothed the hair back from her face. 'Kerry, can you ever forgive me?'

'There's nothing to forgive,' she said simply, feeling as if a great weight were slowly being lifted from her chest. 'You couldn't pretend to love me when you didn't.'

Declan smiled wryly and rubbed his knuckles along her chin. 'No. I couldn't. But I should have understood what was happening. A long time ago I meant to marry you out of habit, charity and a sense of obligation. But maybe in some unacknowledged corner of my mind I knew all along you were meant for me. It's surely true I've never felt the smallest inclination to marry any other woman.'

All at once the room seemed unnaturally quiet. Even Barker had ceased his restless panting. 'Are you saying,' Kerry asked, enunciating each word carefully, 'that you've changed your mind? About marriage? Declan, you never change your mind.'

'Who says I don't? I've even been known to learn from my mistakes.' He grinned, and tipped his head against the back of the chair. 'Yes, Kerry, sweetheart, I have changed my mind.' He slid his hand under her hair.

Kerry held her breath. She wanted to shout, to cry out her joy and hope until all the neighbors for miles around were pounding on the door. But there were three words Declan hadn't spoken.

She waited.

And he said them.

'I love you, Kerry Fleming.'

Five words. They were more than enough. With a small, inarticulate cry, Kerry flung her arms around his neck.

Declan pulled her to him, kissing her eyes, her ears, her nose, and finally her lips. He kissed her with a hungry urgency that stole the breath from her lungs and left her dazed and trembling in his arms. But when it was over he rested his cheek on her hair and said, in a voice choked with emotion and remorse, 'I didn't know, sweetheart.'

'What didn't you know?' she asked gently.

'That love can be as real as a corporate takeover — and infinitely more rewarding. I assumed it was a delusion dreamed up by hormone-crazed adolescents — until I saw that bartender slavering over your cleavage, and wanted to horsewhip the pair of you.'

'Do you own a horse?' Kerry asked warily.

Declan laughed. 'No. Not one of my interests.'

'That's all right then.' After a moment she added, 'Do you mean to tell me just because some other man looked at me, you realized — '

'No.' Declan shook his head. 'No, the ultimate revelation hit me when that animated rug tried to knock you over. And I caught you in my arms, and saw the loneliness and desperation in your eyes. I knew then that what I felt for you was more than just a craving for your body . . . Although I do mean to get to that.' He patted her thigh. 'It was a need to be with you, to be there for you when you need me. To share your life — the good, the bad and — ' He sighed. 'In your case, no doubt, the crazy. Perhaps one day to father your children — '

Kerry shook her head. She was smiling and she didn't think she'd ever be able to stop. 'The crazy?' she said. 'You, the corporate man, are willing to take on the crazy?'

Declan laughed and ran a finger down her nose. 'Yes, and I'll probably lose my mind before you do. I know you'll drive me wild at times, Kerry. And you'll be furious with me every time I try to tell you what to do. But I love you *because* you're you. I always will.'

'And I love you,' replied Kerry. 'I think I always have.'

'Are you sure? Very sure? Because I'm not going to change, Kerry.' He heaved an exaggerated sigh. 'Nor, I fear, are you.'

'Of course I'm not,' she said airily. 'But don't worry, it'll be all right. We'll complement each other. You'll see.'

'That's what I'm afraid of,' said Declan. He tugged gently at a lock of her hair. 'Now tell me — what disruptions do you have in mind for our wedding?'

'Disruptions?' Kerry repeated suspiciously.

'Mmm.' Declan leaned his head back and grinned up at her. 'I'm thinking that to be on the safe side, I ought to post an armed guard outside the church. I'm not having you whipped out from under my nose again, Kerry Fleming. This time I plan to keep what I've got.' He gave her a slow, curving smile that turned her limp with lust.

'You needn't worry,' she gasped. 'This time I won't try to get away.'

'You won't get the chance.'

But when Kerry said, 'Good,' and began to unbutton his shirt, Declan tipped her off his knee and stood up.

'Food,' he said briskly. 'It seems to me we missed lunch.'

Somewhere in the background, Barker thumped his tail.

'Lunch?' said Kerry. 'But I thought — '

He held up his hand. 'Don't. Not this time. Just go to the kitchen, put your head in the fridge and think healthy thoughts about cabbage.'

'Cabbage?' repeated Kerry blankly. 'I don't want to think about cabbage.'

'I know. Neither do I. But if I allow my thoughts to follow their natural inclinations, I'm liable to find myself spending several hours in a very cold shower.' He smiled crookedly. 'If cabbage doesn't do it, try parsnips. They work for me. So does tapioca.'

Kerry shook her head in exasperation. 'Declan, what are you talking about? I don't want to think about vegetables. Or puddings. I want to think about you.' She reached for him, but he caught her wrists and held her away.

'Thank you. I'm flattered. Now do as

I say and think parsnips.' His voice was firm, not the kind of voice that brooked argument.

'Declan, stop it,' cried Kerry, beginning to lose her temper. Her emotions had been through more than enough turmoil for one day. 'What have vegetables got to do with anything?'

'Nothing,' he admitted. 'What I'm trying to get through your head, sweetheart, is that, tempting as I know I'm going to find it, I am not going to bed with you before we're married. I've spent too many years keeping you out of trouble to let us both down at this stage.'

'But I've already *been* married,' protested Kerry.

'I know. But, you see, I haven't.'

Kerry sighed. She recognized that note of obdurate inflexibility. Declan, the man who always did things his way, would do what he thought was right to the bitter end.

And she loved him for it.

'OK. Cabbage it is,' she said glumly.

'That's my girl.' Declan dropped her wrists and patted her approvingly on the rear. 'You know, something tells me I'm going to be very tired of cabbage — and parsnips — by the time our wedding day rolls around.'

'Me, too,' said Kerry with feeling. She paused. 'I suppose all this nonsense about vegetables is your idea of a suitable revenge. Because I married Larry.'

'No,' Declan replied without hesitation. 'My idea of a suitable revenge will be to show you just exactly what you missed by not marrying me when you had the chance.' He grinned wickedly. 'And I promise you my revenge will be sweet. I'll look forward to it.'

'So will I,' said Kerry with a sigh. Declan's principles might be admirable, but they were desperately hard on her libido. She put her hands on his shoulders and lifted her lips for his kiss.

When it came, it was unbearably brief, and followed by a quick shove toward the door.

'Lunch, Kerry.' Declan's voice was low and unusually thick.

Good. He was going to find this unnecessary celibacy as hard to put up with as she was. 'All right,' she replied jauntily. 'I'll see what I can do about the cabbage. I hope you'll find it warm and willing.'

Declan's shout of outrage was cut off by the firm click of the door.

★ ★ ★

The church was packed. Not as packed as it had been seven years ago when the population of Carmody Falls had first gathered to witness the wedding of Kerry Fleming to Declan King — but full enough. Once again Declan stood tall and stiff before the altar, and as the music of the organ soared to the high arch of the ceiling, once again he turned to Harry and murmured, 'Here comes the bride. Late as usual.'

But this time, instead of looking uncomfortable, Harry grinned. 'Count yourself lucky,' he muttered out of the side of his mouth. 'At least this time she won't run off with the wrong groom.'

'No,' agreed Declan. 'But knowing Kerry, she'll find some other way to enliven the proceedings.'

The Reverend Jonathan MacNaughton-Bones cleared his throat discreetly and frowned, and Declan turned to watch Kerry glide down the aisle on the arm of his beaming father, who had given up a week's bridge for the occasion.

Kerry smiled lovingly at the man who was soon to be her husband and wondered how she could ever have married anyone else. When he returned her smile with the crooked tenderness that was uniquely Declan, she felt her pulses speed up in anticipation.

The weeks they had spent preparing for this day had not been easy, and many times Kerry had had to restrain herself from attempting to seduce Declan on the nearest pile carpet or patch of earth. She would probably have tried it if she'd thought she had a hope of getting past the resolution he had formed so long ago of keeping Kerry Fleming respectable.

But now, soon, the waiting would be over. And as usual, Declan had proved right. He was a man worth waiting for. In spite of her initial impatience, or perhaps because of it, she was glad they had done it his way.

'Dearly beloved, we are gathered here in the sight of God . . . '

Kerry started, and after giving her soon-to-be husband one last beatific smile, she turned to face the sonorous-voiced clergyman who stood waiting to pronounce her Declan's wife.

Fifteen minutes later, after a delay that had lasted seven years, Kerry Fleming was finally married to Declan King.

Some hours after that, when the goodbyes had all been said and the well-wishers had finally left for home, Kerry and Declan were once again together in a car as he drove smoothly down the highway to Thunder Bay.

From there they planned to catch a plane to Toronto where they would be boarding a flight to the Greek Isles. 'By ourselves. No dogs,' Declan had said earlier, referring to Barker, who was temporarily in the capable hands of Phil and his soon-to-be-bride, Maybelle Jensen.

Declan sat with one hand resting loosely on the wheel and his free arm draped around Kerry. As they sped along the undulating road with its low cliffs and miles of uncut trees, he announced suddenly, 'Kerry, I have something to tell you.'

Kerry looked up. 'Yes. What is it?'

'Your shop. I'm sorry you had to give it up for me — '

'I didn't. I gave it up for me. I can always open another bookshop.'

Declan fixed his gaze on the pale gray ribbon of the highway. 'That's just it. You can't.'

'Now listen,' said Kerry, feeling the hair on her neck rise in indignation. 'We've only been married a few hours, and if you think you're going to start by bossing me around — '

'I,' interrupted Declan, 'am only bossy when sorely provoked.' He sighed. 'As no doubt I frequently will be. But keep your shirt on. I want the privilege of removing it myself. And I'm not even attempting to boss you around. Yet.'

'Then what are you talking about?' asked Kerry, mystified.

'I bought you another bookstore. In Toronto. I had it checked out, and it seems financially sound.'

'Oh,' gasped Kerry. 'I was dreading the business of starting all over again. If it took as much work as it did the last time . . . ' She broke off. 'Thank you. Oh, Declan, I do love you.' Overcome with love and gratitude, Kerry raised her arms to throw them around his neck.

But Declan, seeing what was coming, said, 'No, Kerry. Not again,' with a severity convincing enough to make her hesitate. At once he pulled the car to a stop beneath a stand of bright green maples beside the road.

He counted to ten. Slowly. Then he turned to Kerry, who was busy avoiding his eye, and said in a voice that, in the circumstances, was remarkably restrained, 'Kerry, sweetheart, it's just as well I didn't marry you for a quiet life, because I can see I'm not going to get one. But I would like to make it to the honeymoon.' He touched her cheek and made her look at him. When her anxious eyes met his, he added softly, 'And just to be sure, I think we'd better start on it at once.' He put his hand on her thigh and, with a low cry, Kerry reached for him and pulled his face to hers. Their lips met — and if they hadn't been in a car on the public highway, they would have climbed her rainbow to the moon right then and there.

As it was, by the time they were on their way again, the evening was already drawing in. 'You'll have to speed up if we're going to make our flight,' said Kerry.

'No problem. There's always tomorrow.'

So there was. 'Yes,' she agreed. 'And tomorrow and tomorrow and — Declan, there's a kitten by the side of the road. Do you think it's lost?'

'No,' said Declan, speeding up. He tried not to look at his new wife. But in the end he couldn't help himself.

One glance at her face was enough.

With a groan of resignation, he stopped the car and switched it into reverse.

THE END

We do hope that you have enjoyed reading this large print book.

Did you know that all of our titles are available for purchase?

We publish a wide range of high quality large print books including:
Romances, Mysteries, Classics General Fiction Non Fiction and Westerns

Special interest titles available in large print are:
The Little Oxford Dictionary Music Book, Song Book Hymn Book, Service Book

Also available from us courtesy of Oxford University Press:
Young Readers' Dictionary (large print edition) Young Readers' Thesaurus (large print edition)

For further information or a free brochure, please contact us at:
**Ulverscroft Large Print Books Ltd., The Green, Bradgate Road, Anstey, Leicester, LE7 7FU, England.
Tel:** (00 44) **0116 236 4325
Fax:** (00 44) **0116 234 0205**

Other titles in the
Linford Romance Library:

TERESA'S TREASURE

Valerie Holmes

Teresa, as a child, dreamt of the day when the secret inside a tin box would be revealed to her. However, as she grows into a young woman her life changes dramatically, shattering her childhood dreams . . . yet she still remembers her treasure. Risking a possible marriage match, Teresa decides to go on a journey of discovery to seek it out. But some secrets are meant to stay buried. What she discovers is of greater value than she had ever imagined.

THE SHOWMAN'S GIRL

Julia Douglas

When Emily runs away with the circus in the 1930s, she enters a magical world of perilous adventures, intense friendships and deep passions. Growing up in the big top, she admires, from afar, the charismatic showman, Adam Strand. But Adam is torn between his wife Jayne, a daredevil tight-wire walker, and Molly, the elephant trainer who's always carried a torch for him. Emily becomes a star — but will she ever be able to tell Adam how she really feels?

A PERFECT ARRANGEMENT

Kay Gregory

'You'd suit me very well. You're tidy, you're intelligent, you're unlikely to vamp me . . . And you can type!' Hardly the most flattering description Holly had ever heard — but for all Ethan Yorke's arrogance — his job offer *was* tempting. And plain Holly, in her business suits and glasses, knew that she was safe . . . Ethan would never look twice at her! So why did she have to go and do a foolish thing like falling in love with him?

DARE TO LOVE

Chrissie Loveday

Back in 1930, when Nellie marries James, the owner of a pottery factory, her future looks wonderful. However, moving into a different social class brings its issues. She is now the mistress of the house, where once she was a lowly maidservant, and, despite being able to help her family financially, they have their own problems in life and she can never resist interfering. But with her strength of character and talents, she will usually win the day . . .

SECOND CHANCE

Kate Jackson

Laura Sinclair's return to Orkney turns out to be far more complicated than she had expected. She's confronted with family secrets and meets the one person she wanted to avoid — her former love, Matt. While she waits to find out which direction her career will take, Laura takes on the challenge of helping her family whilst having to face up to her past actions — and Matt . . .